How

Virtual Reality Adv
a big difference. T
or die doesn't depe

To start your adventure simply choose your character
from the list on pages 7 and 8. Each character has a
unique selection of four skills; these skills will decide
which options are available to you.

Fill in the skills of your chosen character on the
Adventure Sheet on page 6. Also note your Life Points
and your possessions.

Life Points are lost each time you are wounded. If you
are ever reduced to zero Life Points, you have been
killed and the adventure ends. Sometimes you can
recover Life Points during the adventure, but you can
never have more Life Points than you started with.

You can carry up to eight possessions at a time. If you
are at this limit and find something else you want, drop
one of your other possessions (by crossing it off your
Adventure Sheet) to make room for the new item.

Consider your selection of skills. They establish your
special strengths, and will help you to role-play your
choices during the adventure. If you arrive at an entry
which lists options for more than one of your skills, you
can choose which skill to use in that situation.

That's all you need to know. Now choose your character.

Virtual Reality *titles to test your skills*

Green Blood

Mark Smith

Illustrated by Terry Oakes

MAMMOTH

Published 1993 by Mammoth
an imprint of Reed Consumer Books Limited
Michelin House, 81 Fulham Road, London SW3 6RB
and Auckland, Melbourne, Singapore and Toronto

Text copyright © 1993 Dave Morris and Mark Smith
Illustrations copyright © 1993 Terry Oakes
Map copyright © 1993 Leo Hartas

ISBN 0 7497 1484 0

A CIP catalogue record for this title is available from the British Library

Printed in Great Britain by Cox and Wyman Ltd, Reading

CONTENTS

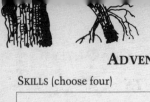

ADVENTURE SHEET

SKILLS (choose four)

LIFE POINTS

Initial Score _____

POSSESSIONS (maximum of 8)

NOTES AND CODEWORDS

MONEY

CHOOSE ONE OF THESE CHARACTERS

The Duellist

Skills: AGILITY, FOLKLORE, ROGUERY and SWORDPLAY
Profile: As a professional duellist you have upset too many people by winning the spoils of your contests, and you must move on.
Life Points: 10
Possessions: Sword
Money: 10 gold pieces

The Ranger

Skills: ARCHERY, STREETWISE, SWORDPLAY and WILDERNESS LORE
Profile: Being loyal to the traditional values of your forefathers, you protect those forced to journey off the road.
Life Points: 11
Possessions: Longbow, sword
Money: 10 gold pieces

The Monk

Skills: AGILITY, SPELLS, UNARMED COMBAT and WILDERNESS LORE
Profile: The monks who taught you skills have been driven out and you are persecuted for your faith. Life is harsh but you endure all hardships.
Life Points: 11
Possessions: Magic wand
Money: 8 gold pieces

The Sorcerer's Apprentice

Skills: CHARMS, FOLKLORE, SPELLS and WILDERNESS LORE
Profile: Sold to a warlock when you were a child, your knowledge eventually outstripped your master's.
Life Points: 9
Possessions: Magic amulet, magic wand
Money: 12 gold pieces

The Starveling

Skills: CUNNING, ROGUERY, STREETWISE and UNARMED COMBAT
Profile: Orphaned in childhood, you made your way half-starved to the city. You learned what it takes to survive in this uncaring world, but now you want to seek something worthwhile in your life...
Life Points: 10
Possessions: None
Money: 15 gold pieces

The Traveller

Skills: FOLKLORE, ROGUERY, SWORDPLAY and WILDERNESS LORE
Profile: You never knew your father, and your mother mislaid you among the carts of a slaver's caravan. Cities make you ill; you can only breath freely on the open road.
Life Points: 10
Possessions: Sword
Money: 10 gold pieces

The Thief

Skills: AGILITY, ARCHERY, CUNNING and ROGUERY
Profile: You are secretive and restless, always just one jump ahead of the hangman's noose. Your latest exploit has made the city too dangerous for you and you must lie low.
Life Points: 10
Possessions: Longbow, two jewels
Money: 16 gold pieces

Alternatively design your own character, taking any four skills of your choice from the Glossary of Skills on page 9. Your character will also have any possessions needed for the skills chosen (e.g. a wand if you choose SPELLS) and will start with 10 gold pieces. Your initial Life Points score will be 10.

GLOSSARY OF SKILLS

AGILITY
The ability to perform acrobatic feats, run, climb, balance and leap. A character with this skill is nimble and dexterous.

ARCHERY
A long-range attack skill. You must possess a longbow to use this skill

CHARMS
The expert use of magical wards to protect you from danger. Also includes that most elusive of qualities: luck. You must possess a magic amulet to use this skill.

CUNNING
The ability to think on your feet and devise clever schemes for getting out of trouble. Useful in countless situations.

FOLKLORE
Knowledge of myth and legend, and how best to deal with supernatural menaces such as garlic against vampires, silver bullets against a werewolf, and so on.

ROGUERY
The traditional repertoire of a thief's tricks: picking pockets, opening locks, and skulking unseen in the shadows.

SPELLS
A range of magical effects encompassing illusions, elemental effects, commands, and summonings. You must possess a magic wand to use this skill.

STREETWISE
With this skill you are never at a loss in towns and cities. What others see as the squalor and menace of narrow cobbled streets is home to you.

SWORDPLAY
The best fighting skill. You must possess a sword to use this skill.

UNARMED COMBAT
Fisticuffs, wrestling holds, jabs and kicks, and the tricks of infighting. Not as effective as SWORDPLAY, but you do not need weapons – your own body is the weapon!

WILDERNESS LORE
A talent for survival in the wild – whether it be forest, desert, swamp or mountain peak.

PROLOGUE

Sickened by the ways of your fellow men and despairing of man's cruelty, you have quit the teeming city of Godorno, with its cesspools and plague pits, its beggars and abject slaves. You walk for days, revelling in the fresh air of the countryside. This is a green land of hills and dales, farmsteads and mills – a veritable bread-basket that yields all its grains and fruit to the decadent city.

As you walk you have much time to think. Long ago your family told you how the star of destiny, purple Praxis, changed colour to the flaming gold of Moraine, God of War, at the moment of your birth. Even as Praxis flared with energy, so your mother's life waned. She died of exhaustion bringing you into the world, but her sisters looked after you until you were old enough, at eight, to go up to the dreaming spires of the academy at Hegalopolis.

The bookish scholars trained you in many things and all who taught there agreed you showed great promise. But when you were just fifteen years old, Gornild, the harsh overlord of Godorno, dissolved all the monasteries in the lands along the Marches, fearing their teachings would turn minds against his corrupt rule. You were forced to scratch out a miserable living just like the other poor folk of the city.

The cloistered life of the academy, with its politeness and order, gave you scant preparation for life on the streets of Godorno. You developed the cunning of a sewer rat and the patience of the damned just staying alive from day to day, dodging the press gangs from the war galleys that carry young men off to fight the corsairs. Your cunning was great enough to avoid the fate of the galley slave and you have grown to maturity, strong, tough and determined.

The ways of the city folk revolt you. Your diligent study of history shows an ever churning cycle of oppressors and the downtrodden. Man is strapped to the wheel of fate to be alternately dragged to the heights and plunged again into the pits and windblasted depths of pain and want.

As you walk, every step that bears you away from the stench of the city is a step taken more lightly than the last. You resolve to return to the city only if you have changed things for the better. Yours is the nobleness of spirit that would lay down its life to better the lot of your fellow man. If Praxis robbed you of a mother's love, Praxis can repay the debt by shining brightly on your destiny.

As the miles pass with you deep in thought, your path takes you inexorably on towards the great forest, beyond the lands of men. Your curiosity has been piqued by rumours and legends about the ancient Tree of Knowledge, a fabled tree hundreds of feet high, with golden bark and silver leaves. It is said to grow at the centre of the great Forest of Arden.

Fey sylvan elves are said to dwell there. The stories of what they look like and the fate that befalls those lost in the forest are too fantastically horrific to be true. Each fable tells a different story: of elves with six arms, of elves with scimitar blades in place of forearms, and of greenbark bows that can send an arrow from one horizon to the other and which always hit their mark. And there are stories of elves with jewels for eyes which melt when they cry, as cry they must when disturbed by man, for they keenly sense the tragedy of man's mortality.

Though each story is fanciful and bizarre they all agree in one respect. No one who sees the elves lives to tell of it. There isn't a man alive who has glimpsed the splendid glory of Elvenhame, the city of the elves.

You no longer know whether it is the desire to see elves or your wish to change the world for the better that takes you on your quest. What, however, if you were to learn the knowledge of ages and return to the lands of men as a saviour? Your name would go down in history. Anything less magnificent than this noble quest for the knowledge that will save mankind will not do. You will become a hero or die in the attempt.

You are on the road. It is approaching early evening and purple Praxis already beams out in the low dusk sky. As you stare at the star, it seems to wink out then flare bright golden yellow before resuming its usual purple form. It is a sign that your destiny awaits in the Forest of Arden.

Now turn to **1**.

The road tops a ridge that is straddled by the ruins of a great wall, half covered in turf. The wall once marked the border between the lands of man and domain of the elves. Quickly you scramble up and over the blocks of fallen stone. Standing atop the ruin, you survey the outlands beyond.

Your gaze sweeps across the broad patches of purple heather and yellow gorse that cover the inhospitable uplands. The air smells fresh; it is good to be free of the noisome taint of the sewers and plague pits of the city you have left behind. The road winds down into a valley, at the foot of which nestles Burg, a small town of neat white houses with roofs of triangular grey slates. Here may be your last chance to talk with mankind before you are swallowed up by the depths of the great Forest of Arden.

As you walk towards the buildings through the tilled and reaped land of the valley, you pass gleaners – peasants who search the ground for stalks of straw and seed spilled during the harvest. The townsfolk, seemingly wary of outsiders, keep out of your way. Ahead of you is an inn, the largest building in the town. Looking forward to perhaps your last night's sleep in a proper bed for many weeks, you make for this hostelry.

The inn seems surprisingly large for a town that is at the very edge of the wilderness. It must once have been a baronial hall built by a lord seeking to carve out a kingdom beyond the great wall. As you walk down the main street the ruddy sky is turning

violet with the onset of twilight. What looked an
inviting little town by day seems sombre and unwel-
coming at nightfall. As you linger a moment outside
the inn, there is a crack of thunder and it begins to
pour with rain.

Inside the inn a young girl is lighting oil lamps
with a taper. Until your eyes grow accustomed to
the gloom you cannot make out who shares the
common room with you, nor many details of the
interior of the inn itself.

You can wait by the door until you can see better
(turn to **37**) or step in and warm yourself before the
fire (turn to **55**).

2

'It is the forest which cleans and purifies the air for
all the world to breathe. Without the Forest of Arden
all living things would choke, gag and die. The trees
absorb the foul air of man's pollution, his burning
and wasting, and give it back to the world again
clean, fresh and ready to breathe. The stench and
dross of the cities is purged and cleansed by the trees.
The forest is the lifeblood of the world.'

The old woman delivers these words very
gravely, convincing you that she believes every word
of what she is saying. All the time her eyes never
leave yours.

'Ah, but I see I bore you. Enough of this idle
prattle, I must take my rest. Good night to you.'

So saying, she gets up and makes to leave you.
You are about to protest that you are far from bored,

but realize she is only looking for a polite way to leave your company. You let her go and decide to take a room at the inn as well. Turn to **333**.

3

A figure lies dead in the forest. Ants crawl in and out of its newly picked-clean eye sockets; beetles and rats gnaw at the remains. With a shock you realize the figure is wearing identical clothes to yours – there isn't another pair of boots in the world quite like yours, made to order by a cobbler in Godorno.

'You are not wearing my ring,' says Elanor. 'If you cannot trust me, I cannot aid you. You must find your own way and I must continue my search for the saviour of the forest. Begone and never come back, you weak-willed doubter.'

Elanor and the owl disappear. You are on your own again. Turn to **70**.

4

Valerian's voice is markedly different from the guttural speech of the Westermen, but there is no doubt that he has thrown in his lot with them. It is plain they depend upon him for their knowledge of the forest and its many dangers. They are planning how to destroy and burn the whole forest tree by tree. Valerian has convinced the Chief of the Westermen that his realm will not be safe until every tree, every sapling and every bush in the forest has been razed to the ground.

'You wanted to tell me something of note, Valerian? Else why have I summoned all my advisers?'

'Indeed, sire, I have a plan to destroy the forest at a stroke.'

'What stroke?'

'By killing the Tree of Life at the very centre of the forest. Slay the Tree of Life, sire, and the whole forest, along with everything in it, will die.'

'Well, your advice has been sound in the past, Valerian. I will do as you suggest and slay the Tree of Life.'

Write the codeword *Bullhorn* on your Adventure Sheet.

If you want to interrupt and tell the chief that the death of the forest will mean death and destruction for the whole world, including him, turn to **198**. If you wish to sneak out of the pavilion and leave while the going is good, turn to **38**.

5

As Valerian stands up, he lets his cloak fall to the floor, revealing armour made of quilted leather – light armour that wouldn't stop a sword thrust. He has no sword or obvious weapon to hand. Three small coloured pouches swing from his belt.

If you decide to hold your ground, turn to **27**. If you want to close with him, turn to **65**.

6

You call out the dragon's name. Its great head rears slowly above you and its yellow-green eyes bore into yours. Its nostrils dilate as it sucks in a deep breath. Too late, you realize you lied to yourself about knowing the creature's name. There is a terrible whooshing that sounds like the dragon's real name as it breathes acid and gas upon you. The torrent of gas and air rolls you across the ground and you are lucky to bang your head on a rock, sparing yourself a more painful death. The Forest of Arden is doomed.

7

You say the word and vanish. Your invisibility, however, doesn't help you deal with the Infernal Statue, whose sword is still chopping into the Tree of Life. You are wasting precious time. Which spell will you cast to help save the tree?

You can cast Choking Fog (turn to **346**), Bafflement (turn to **113**), Visceral Disruption (turn to **64**), or Tower of Will (turn to **186**).

8

The Kwerrel is delighted with his shiny golden disks of metal, which he starts trying to weave into his hair. Now that he has got what he wants he scampers away, leaving you alone inside the bush. The archway back to the forest has reappeared so you make good your escape from the bush.

Turn to **406**.

9

'I must test your fitness to be the forest's saviour,' says Elanor. 'I hope you pass the test. You would not like to see the forest laid to waste would you?'

She looks regal and yet kind, but her eyes never leave yours.

If you reply that your reason for visiting the forest is to find the Tree of Knowledge and take some of its wisdom away with you to the lands of men, turn to **24**. Or will you say that the forest is too beautiful to be laid waste and you will try to save it (turn to **40**)?

10

'Then why have you disturbed my slumber? You have woken me a year early. Now I will feel sick for the next year.' The dragon rolls over and seems to be going back to sleep.

If you wish to attack it, turn to **59**. If you want to try to steal some of its treasure, turn to **79**. If you prefer to continue your quest and leave the dragon to slumber, turn to **49**.

11

You know without doubt that your best plan is to call upon the dragon that has promised its help. Certain in the knowledge that it will obey you, you set off for the Bonehill to enlist its help.

The journey passes swiftly with the help of an elf to guide you, and you are soon at the dragon's lair. You call out its name . . .

Turn to **83**.

12

You tell Pozzo that to escape the forest he should make for a river and follow it to the sea. You know there is a city or town at every river mouth for hundreds of miles around, and when he reaches one he can take ship for Godorno. He bids you farewell and says you may stay as his honoured guest at his inn in Burg if you are ever travelling that way again. With that, he sets out to return to his beloved daughter.

You are soon safe back in the forest, and alone again. The awful sights and sounds of the Westerman camp are soon left far behind. You can head west (turn to **43**), east (turn to **427**), south-west (turn to **70**), or south (turn to **78**).

13

All is quiet behind you but you do not look back. The path is difficult, overgrown and boggy. Every now and then you are hard put to decide which way it leads, but by keeping fairly close to the great river you make progress for many hours until nightfall.

The noises of the forest seem to intensify with night: there is buzzing, clicking, croaking and the hoot of a lone owl to keep you company. Finding a dry place to rest is not easy but at last you find a mound of earth on which you can settle down.

If you have CHARMS and wish to turn your pendant into a warning stone, turn to **361**. Otherwise, turn to **419**.

'Yes it would, more terrible than you can know. The stench and dross of the cities is purged and cleansed by the forest. The trees absorb the foul air of man's pollution, his burning and smelting, and give it back to the world again clean, fresh and ready to breathe. The forest is the lifeblood of the world; without it the world will choke, gag and die. The sin of man, his waste, his poisons, are made good again by the life force of nature. You feel something of this, don't you?' The woman looks at you approvingly.

Sensing that you can trust her, you ask about the Tree of Knowledge.

'If you come to my bower in the forest I can take you to the Great Tree. But I must warn you that if you harm so much as a leaf on your way there you will never leave the forest. When you enter the forest follow the Burgstream to the great Sirion river and then walk down the eastern bank. My followers will bring me word of your progress.'

She takes up her staff and taps it once on the table. Her gnarled old staff turns into a little flute, which she hands to you with the words, 'Blow this at need in the forest and my friends will help you.'

You murmur your thanks and fall to wondering how she can make the animals of the forest do her bidding. As the fire burns down, the woman goes to sleep in her chair. Not wishing to disturb her, you take a room at the inn for the night.

Note the maple flute on your Adventure Sheet and turn to **333**.

15

The imp puts on the emerald ring as if it were a bracelet, and then tries to rip it off again. But the band of gold constricts until it is a perfect fit around his wrist.

'Alack, alack, I can never take this cursed thing off,' the imp laments.

'Help me, and I will remove the ring.'

'I am the Kwerrel, and the Kwerrel keeps no bargains.'

'Then you are a prisoner of the Lady of the Forest's ring for ever and every being in the forest will know that you are not her friend,' you say.

Quailing at your words, the Kwerrel says, 'Take the flesh of the toadstool. Make an infusion with elderflower wine and give it to any being you wish to drug into sleep. They will sleep the sleep of the damned. Look, now I open the archway for you to leave.'

As the imp speaks the gold ring grows and falls from his wrist to lie on the ground near the giant toadstool. You pick it up again, take a large piece of the flesh of the toadstool. Bidding the little imp goodbye, you walk back into the forest.

Add the toadstool flesh to the list of possessions on your Adventure Sheet. Then turn to **406**.

16

You walk across the room without looking to either side, pretending not to have heard the command.

The same voice rings out again, but the imperious tone now carries the sharp ring of anger: 'So you think you can come here and treat us as though we are beneath notice, do you? Are you deaf? Ignore Valerian, would you? I'll make you pay for your insolence.'

There is a scramble as people leave the common room. Only the old woman in grey stays to watch the fight. It is too late to do anything but fight or run.

If you run out of the inn without looking back, turn to **117**. Otherwise you must fight, turn to **5**.

17

The odds are stacked against you as more and more guards pour into the pavilion. Together with the chief's advisers they easily overwhelm you, forcing you to your knees before the chief. The Westermen's leader reaches for his sword, draws it back and drives it into your heart, smiling evilly as he does so. As you die, so too do the hopes of saving the Forest of Arden.

18

As you voice acceptance of the duel, a hundred of the most wise and ancient-looking elves appear silently from the trees at the edge of the clearing. They fan out, encircling you completely, and with their feet scrape a circle in the dirt at the clearing's edge.

All the elves are typical of their kind, with long wine-red hair and pale green skin that has a silvery bloom. Their clothes, in shades of green and brown, blends with the backdrop of the forest and makes it seem as if the very trees have walled you into the clearing. If you get beyond that ring, you feel it will only ever be as vanquisher of the elves' champion, whoever that might be.

'If you step outside the circle you have lost,' states the King of the Elves. 'When you have decided how you will fight, I will choose a champion from all elvenkind to face you.'

If you have SPELLS and wish to try out the potency of your magic against that of the immortal elves, turn to **33**. If you have SWORDPLAY and wish to try your skill with the sword against the champion of all the elves, turn to **50**. If you have UNARMED COMBAT and wish to pit your body against one of the lithe quick elves, turn to **63**. If you have none of these skills, you will have to concede defeat: turn to **163**.

19

The dragon bats you out of the cavern and sends you rolling down the bank like a golden cannonball. You struggle to your feet while the ancient beast mocks you.

'It is a long time since I spied a golden turtle in these parts.' He laughs and hisses as you stagger away from the Bonehill.

Weighed down by gold, you have no chance of completing your quest unless you head back to Burg and find someone to remove the precious metal. No matter, you will be rich beyond your wildest dreams . . . Turn to **39**.

20

He points up at the sun shining down on the clearing. Spitting onto his finger, he flicks the saliva up into the air. To your astonishment, a green watery film covers the face of the sun. It lasts only an instant before being wiped away like the blinking of a giant celestial eye. The Elf King turns to you, and his feral smile is brimming with triumph. 'Can you do that, mortal? Make the sun go green?'

If you have SPELLS and a wand, you can cast an illusion to achieve the desired effect and pass the Elf King's test, turn to **232**. Otherwise you must admit defeat: turn to **69**.

21

With the dragon's help and the might of the elves, you feel you have a chance of defeating the forces of the Westerman and driving the threat of their evil from the forest. Full of confidence in your ability to call upon a powerful ally of the ancient times, you head towards the rowan trees at the edge of the forest.

Travelling along routes that seem to come unbidden to your mind, you reach a clearing that seems strangely familiar. Was it here perhaps, that you met the elves? Or does some horror of your travels lurk nearby in the undergrowth?

Summoning up your courage, you call out to whoever or whatever will hear: 'Elves! If you would win your freedom, come talk with a mortal who can deliver it. For I have secured us an ally equal to half the Westerman's forces – a dragon whose very appearance will slay scores of them from sheer terror. Come forward and speak with me.'

The words of your challenge die away, suffocated by the preternatual silence of the forest. You might have expected to hear the chirruping voice of a bird, or the faint rustle of a woodmouse questing for beetles, yet there is nothing. Cursing the elves for their arrogance, you shout again, 'Come forward!'

Spittle flies from your lips and your face flushes with the violent passion of your request. Again you wait for a reply.

'Do you think that one dragon is enough, then, to beat your fellow men?' says a cool voice from behind you.

Spinning around, you see no more than inches from your face the eternally youthful face of an elf. Yet the penetrating eyes that are windows to the wisdom of countless centuries mark this elf out above all others. The Elf King has answered your call.

'One dragon is more than enough,' you reply, 'with the forces of the elves as well. He will demoralize the Westermen, plunging them into chaos from which the deadly arrows of the elves will cruelly pluck them.'

He smiles a cold smile, approving of the relish with which you describe the Westermen's deaths. 'Brave words indeed, for a mortal. But for the elves to accede to your schemes and counsels, you must prove yourself worthy of our respect.'

'How may I do that?'

'Overcome my champion in a duel. Only then will we heed your words.'

If you have FOLKLORE, turn to **215**. If not, but you have the codeword *Speculum*, turn to **309**. If you have neither, it seems you must accept his terms – turn to **137**.

22

The sprite inclines your own reflected face in an expression of deep meditation. 'I see your destiny,' it says at last. 'You will either prove yourself a hero, saving the forest, or else you will allow venality and pride to lead you to your doom.'

'Being a hero sounds the better option,' you comment drily.

'In that case, you must seek Elanor the Grey Lady. Solitude has made her strange – not quite elvish in her ways, but not human any longer either. But you should trust her, as she'll set you on the right path. Then you must find the elves. Convincing them to help you may prove a weighty task, for they are proud and aloof and wilfully headstrong. Next seek the camp of the Westermen to learn their plans. They will destroy the forest if they succeed, and only direct action can stop them. Perhaps you can dig up a worm to help you.'

There is a long pause. You look expectantly at the reflection until it finally gives you a distinctly unhuman grin. 'Well, that is the prophecy,' it concludes.

Will you now keep your promise to break the mirror (turn to **418**) or leave it intact for the time being (turn to **105**)?

23

The Infernal Statue is belching steam as its sword arm rises and falls like a piston. As you do not wish to attack the steaming statue directly, what will you do?

You can attack the shieldbearers and bodyguards clustered around the great boiler (turn to **203**) or try to get to the pipe that connects the Infernal Statue to the boiler (turn to **397**).

24

'The hackers and burners, the men from the west, say the ants of the forest must be eradicated because they eat the farmers' crops,' she says. 'What do you say?'

If you say the ants are indeed pests and should be wiped out, turn to **51**. If you reply that the forest would choke and die if there were no ants to eat the dead leaves and wood, turn to **67**. If you have WILDERNESS LORE, you can turn to **171**.

25

The Chief of the Westermen describes his favourite toy to you. His eyes are shining with enthusiasm as he describes a great steam-powered machine of metal armour inside which a man can ride. The suit is as large as a giant and as powerful as a steam hammer, it can smash men to pulp or rend them limb from limb. The chief believes it works by magic.

'It only has one weakness. Sever the line that connects it to the steam furnace and it dies. Only a real hero could stand up to The Steamer and do that, by the gods.'

At that moment a visitor is announced. 'It is Valerian the Moon Druid, sire,' says the herald. 'He says he has important news. Shall we let him come in?'

'Aye, let him enter.' The speech of the Westermen sounds guttural and uncouth, but you can understand their dialect.

The man who enters is the man you first saw in the inn at Burg. He is still dressed in the black travelling cloak, but his hood is thrown back to reveal his hatchet-like face and pointed black goatee beard. He bows before the chief, then wrinkles his nose and stares at you.

If you wish to make your excuses and leave, turn to **38**. If you choose to stay and hear what important news Valerian brings, turn to **4**.

26

'You have seen what will come to pass if you fail in your quest: death and nothing but death. Now let us see whether your future holds something different in store.'

Elanor takes your hand and brushes the surface of the water with your fingertips. A new picture forms and your eyes grow round with wonder. Something that looks like a hill set between tall dark trees is stirring and turning to look at you. It is a dragon, the oldest of the ancient beasts, not quite immortal. Its red eyes contrast horribly with the smooth jade green scales of its body. It snorts and a cloud of green gas rolls towards you. You jerk back from the vision in horror, before you remember it is just a picture on the water. You see yourself darting away from the cloud. Later, the vision shows you riding astride the creature's back while it flexes its wings in flight.

'You must win over the dragon, the most powerful of all the forest's denizens,' says Elanor. 'Then it will fight for you against the Westermen.'

Turn to **41**.

27

While you hold your ground, Valerian begins casting a spell. If you have SPELLS and a wand then you can either go onto the offensive (turn to **169**) or prepare a defensive magic (turn to **182**). Otherwise, turn to **87**.

28

Fearing death at any moment, plunge your dagger into the rubber hose that connects the great boiler to the Infernal Statue, which is still hacking chunks out of the Tree of Life. The hose breaks and the ends whip round with dreadful force. The Westermen coming to attack you are scythed off their feet by the hose, and you are bathed in a fog of hot steam.

You stagger out of the fog where you were safe, because it is unbearably hot, and watch as the Infernal Statue seems to run down like a clockwork toy. It bends, bows and then rolls down into the deep blue pool. The Westermen give a howl of dismay and begin to retreat, harried by the arrows of the elves.

Turn to **500**.

29

Valerian's attention is distracted by what the king is pointing out on the map. You inch quietly past the guards and towards the pavilion's porchway. Valerian looks up and his eyes narrow, then he cries out, 'There's something moving, they're getting away. I have the senses of a bat.'

He points in your general direction. The guards peer from him to where you stand, unable to make you out.

If you think your best option is to cast the Shield of Defence spell, turn to **441**. Otherwise you can make a run for the forest: turn to **451**.

30

It will take two days to travel from Elvenhame to the Tree of Life. You delay as long as possible, mustering more than seven thousand elves, before setting out to defend the Tree of Life.

The elves fight bravely but they are outnumbered and in hand-to-hand fighting their lack of swords and armour proves a fatal weakness. Green blood flows everywhere.

You perish along with the last of the elves, vainly trying to protect their king. The death of so many immortal elves is the greatest disaster the world has ever witnessed. Nothing can now stop the Westermen reaching the Tree of Life: the Forest of Arden is doomed.

31

A grandiose gesture brings forth the Choking Fog about the machine. But why have you used this spell against a machine that doesn't breathe but is powered by steam? The steam rushing from vents in the head dissipates the fog and the Infernal Statue lurches to the Tree of Life once again, raising its sword arm to strike.

You can cast Bafflement (turn to **113**), Visceral Disruption (turn to **64**), or Tower of Will (turn to **186**).

32

There is another great whooshing exhalation behind you and you start to sprint. The gurgling sounds closer this time. The dragon must be chasing you. Straining your ears, you listen for sounds of the leviathan crashing through the ferns behind, over the rasping of your own breath and the thudding of your feet on the ground. You run until exhaustion over-whelms you but there are no sounds of pursuit now. It seems you have escaped the dragon.

If indeed you are near the Bonehill, the dragon's lair, you will need to travel for several days to the west to regain your course (turn to **43**). If you wish to continue north in your original direction, turn to **127**.

33

'I choose to use magic to fight this duel,' you say, confident that your power is enough to beat any elf.

The King of the Elves smiles when he hears your choice – a cool smile that induces doubt and imbues you with fear. You realize you have never seen an elf smile before; the action transforms the king's face, making him look quite human all of a sudden.

'You think to pit your magic against that of the elves? I will be the champion of elvendom in this duel: I can fashion a spell as well as any other standing here. We will use no death magics. We have potions to revive us if we are wounded. Don't make me kill you; submit if you feel my power overmastering yours.'

With that he gestures you to take up position inside the grassy circle.

Decide whether you will stand with the wind in your face or at your back, and write your choice on your Adventure Sheet.

The Elf King walks solemnly to the other side of the circle and waits confidently.

If you stay in position opposite him, turn to **76**. If you wish to try to get out of the duel by telling the king you should be measured against your foes, the Westermen, instead of the elves you have come to help, turn to **92**.

34

You could not possibly be near the Bonehill, which is several days travel to the east. The whole character of the forest here is very different from the area near the Bonehill. You can, however, at least investigate the area where the whooshing noise came from. Turn to **68**.

35

Elanor, today dressed in a silver gown of gossamer silk, turns to look at you searchingly as you walk underneath the hawthorn arch. She smiles and asks if you are feeling brave today.

You sense a sombre urgency behind her words, and, imitating a courtly bow, you reply, 'My lady, I have never felt more heroic!'

'Good. Do you dare to glimpse your future, my hero?'

You have always avoided fortune-tellers. You have noticed that if a fortune-teller gives good news, people go away happy and expect good fortune to turn up on a plate without them lifting a finger. If the soothsayer prophesies misfortune a sense of helplessness comes over people and they all too often sink into a despairing inactivity which leads to their downfall through sloth. Thus their prophesy is self-fulfilling. It is a well-known fact in Godorno that those soothsayers who always give good auguries are never short of custom, leading you to conclude that they often lie, pretending to see happy events when they should be giving bad news, good fortune when they should be giving bad tidings.

Your worry on this score, however, is soon gone. Looking in the basin of smooth clear water it seems as though an artist is hurriedly painting a picture of ghoulish horror.

'The water shows what will come to pass if you do not succeed in your quest,' says Elanor.

The picture is complete now in terrible detail, as if you were actually looking at the burnt remains of the forest. The trees have been chopped down as far as the eye can see. An infernal engine of some kind belches black smoke. Two hundred paces away you see a forge where a gigantic cauldron is suspended over a bonfire; six men constantly feed the fire with wood and charcoal. All the men working there have very pale skins, their faces long and thin, like hatchets. They shout to each other over the din of the engine in a language you don't understand.

Teams of horses harnessed together pull logs to where groups of men cut them up ready for burning. A row of children sit nearby; they are darker skinned than the men and have been set to toil over sharpening the saws.

Where the trees have been felled and stripped, men are torching the underbrush. They seem intent on killing everything that lives in the forest. A pall of smoke hangs like a storm-cloud over the scene.

Then the vision shifts and the men have gone, leaving behind nothing but the grey ashes of death. All that remains of the forest is a few blackened stumps.

Note the codeword *Crabclaw* on your Adventure Sheet and turn to **26**.

36

The dragon yawns, its fangs raking the sky twenty feet apart. You can see the glands inside its throat that produce the acid and poison for its deadly breath. The ancient beast could kill you in a moment.

If you wish to flee, turn to **165**. If feel brave enough to see what fate it intends for you, turn to **178**.

37

The smoking lamps produce little light, but peering through the gloom you can see several circular tables set about the hall, three near the fire and four back in the shadows. Two men, one tall and the other short and stocky, hog the fire and are engaged in conver-

sation. Several dark figures are seated at the tables. One of these seems to be shrouded in a black travelling cloak.

'You, stranger. Do you fear enemies here? Why skulk in the shadows like a rogue? Step nearer the fire so we may see your face.'

You can't even tell who spoke to you but he doesn't sound friendly.

If you obey the command, turn to **108**. If you ignore it, turn to **16**. If you would rather leave the inn, turn to **117**.

38

Once you are a safe distance from the pavilion, you run for the edge of the trees, quickly hiding yourself in the depths of the forest. The awful sights and sounds of the Westerman camp are soon far behind.

If you have the two codewords *Waterbearer* and *Bullhorn* on your Adventure Sheet, turn to **53**. Otherwise you can head west (turn to **43**), east (turn to **70**), south-west (turn to **270**), or south (turn to **78**) from here.

39

Your plight is hopeless. You will never stagger out of the great forest weighed down as you are. One of the dark denizens of the deepest dark tracts of wood will catch you and skin you for the exotic hide you now wear. You will never escape. Because of your greed, the Forest of Arden is doomed.

40

'The hackers and burners, the men from the west, say the ants of the forest must be eradicated because the ants eat their crops. What do you say?'

If you say the ants are indeed pests and should be wiped out, turn to **75**. If you reply that the forest would choke and die if there were no ants to eat the dead leaves and wood, turn to **67**. If you have WILDERNESS LORE you can turn to **171**.

41

Elanor takes your hand once more and brushes the surface of the water again. The water is icy to your touch this time. A shiver of indefinable apprehension runs through you.

A new picture forms. Elves with bows throng the depths of the forest. They have pale green skin and hair the colour of rich red wine. They are sniping at the Westermen, unseen. Men fall in swathes, pierced by the elves' arrows, but the Westermen come on and on, advancing towards some unseen goal. The elves fall back; it seems they are looking to you to do something decisive.

A terrible figure stalks into view. You can't tell whether it is a man or some infernal magical machine. It looks like a full suit of armour, large enough for a giant of a man, that hisses steam at the joints. It bears a great sword which whistles through the air as it strides mechanically towards you.

The vision fades.

'Your moment of truth, hero. You must be

prepared to fight the smoking man. Remember this vision, saviour, it shows the way to success in your quest,' she says.

She pauses before continuing, 'Tomorrow will be Midsummer's Day. It is time for you to go in search of the elves. But, my hero, you must be careful. Tell them you are a friend of mine and they might not kill you, for they sometimes shoot a man dead with a single arrow before the hapless wanderer knows he is being watched. Harm neither hide nor leaf of the forest. Only by your feeling for nature will the elves judge you. Aside from that they are impartial. You could be a saint or a murderer among men, yet it would count for nothing among the elves.'

When she is sure you know the way she bids you farewell with one last warning. 'The flute will be of no use to you, for I cannot save you from the elves if you anger them. Farewell.'

Turn to **70**.

42

You are in the dark about the plans of Westermen. You can try to find their camp and spy on it, if you have not done so already (turn to **270**), or lead as many of the elves as you can muster in pitched battle against the Westermen (turn to **30**).

43

After several days of trekking west through the forest, and climbing towards uplands, you reach the edge of the Anvil Mountains. Climbing high above the treeline you can see the Forest of Arden laid out beneath you almost like a map. You should have turned south if you wanted to reach the Bonehill, or south-west if you wanted to search for the bower of the Lady of the Forest. As it is you have wasted too much time, and you are far out of your way.

You re-enter the forest, journeying along the paths between its great trees. After the few days, however, you start to find the fresh bodies of hundreds of elves among the trees. It is as though they have all been slain instantly in the act of doing everyday things – some while eating their supper. Whatever has caused this terrible disaster has bereft the forest of life: it is doomed and so are you.

44

You travel on until you reach the next obstacle in your path: a tributary of the Sirion that is spanned by a rope bridge, the only means of crossing the water. The bridge has clearly been tended to recently, as bushes have been hacked back from the stanchions between which it hangs. Tentatively, you step onto the bridge, which holds your weight but sags more and more as you approach its centre.

When you are half-way across, a waterspout erupts from the river beneath you, out of which flails a mass of vegetation ringed with fibrous tentacles. The water was thrown up by an Embracer, which plucks you from the bridge.

If you have UNARMED COMBAT, you can turn to **61**. If you have SWORDPLAY, you can turn to **81**. If you have neither of these skills, turn to **103**.

45

If you are near the dragon and the Bonehill you will need to turn to the right and travel several days to the west.

If you do this, turn to **43**. Or if you want to investigate the area from where the whooshing noise came, turn to **68**.

46

Elanor, today dressed in a silver gown of gossamer silk, turns to look at you searchingly as you walk underneath the hawthorn arch. She smiles at you.

'Well, my hero, do you feel brave today? Is your resolve strong enough to do what is needed of you?'

'I have never felt more heroic, my noble lady,' you reply, although you know in your heart of hearts that you felt considerably braver while you were wearing Elanor's emerald ring.

'Good,' she replies. 'Do you dare to glimpse your future, my hero?'

You have always avoided fortune-tellers. You have noticed that if a fortune-teller gives good news, people go away content and expect good luck to come their way without the need to lift a finger. If bad luck is prophesied, a sense of helplessness afflicts the person and they might sink into a despairing inactivity which leads to poverty and ruin. Thus the prophecy is self-fulfilling. It is well known that those soothsayers who invariably give good auguries are never short of custom, leading you to conclude that they must be pretending to see happy events even when they should be predicting bad news, since they will simply say what people want to hear.

Your doubts in Elanor's case are soon dispelled. Looking into the basin of smooth clear water it seems as though an unseen artist is hurriedly painting a picture of ghoulish horror. Turn to **3**.

47

As you set foot on the hillock you are surprised at how hard the ground feels, although it yields slightly as if a layer of hard rock were resting on mud. The ground is smooth and has a sheen to it: it only looked like grass. The egret stops its cackling and flies off.

If you wish to step back off the mound, turn to **56**. If you want to climb onwards, turn to **66**.

48

Your sword cuts cleanly through the fibres, lopping the tentacles into pieces. The Embracer emits a piercing shriek and subsides once more into the river. You swim to the far bank before the man-eating monster can recover. Turn to **13**.

49

Leaving the blasted valley behind you, you strike north through the forest in search of the camp of the dreaded Westermen. The ground becomes hillocky and uneven. The trees – hollies and elders – are smaller here; you walk on past ever more spindly and sickly trees until you are faced by an impenetrable wall of thorns that rises up like the great cupola dome on top of the cathedral in Godorno.

You skirt the wall, which seems in actuality to be one great bush of thorns. Here and there the denseness of the growing bushes has gathered the remains of dead animals and pushed them out to its perimeter. One little group of bones looks suspiciously like those of a man or elf mouldering on the ground.

Turn to **99**.

50

The King of the Elves momentarily looks disappointed. He then casts his eyes about him to find a champion. A tall old elf stands forward, the first elf you have seen who carries a sword, which is strapped to his back.

He draws the blade from over his head with a

flourish: it is slim with sharp, wavy edges. He looks quizzically at his king, and asks, 'Do we fight to the death, lord? If so, have no fear for me.'

'You will duel until one of you submits or is killed. If you survive we have two of the Lady of the Forest's potions to revive you if you are wounded,' states the king.

To you he adds, 'Don't make Zorolotl kill you. You should submit when you feel his skill with the sword overmastering yours.'

Zorolotl walks to one side of the grassy circle and waits confidently, his sword held aloft.

If you are prepared to fight and wish to take up your position opposite him, turn to **437**. If you wish to try to get out of the duel by protesting you should be measured against your foes, the Westerman, not against the elves you have come to help, turn to **92**.

51

'I am sorry but you have failed the test. You must leave the forest. Begone.'

Elanor strides determinedly away from you, saying as she departs, 'I will set all the birds and the beasts against you. You have four days to leave the forest, never to return.'

If you wish to follow her, turn to **85**. Or if you wish to let her go and follow your own destiny, turn to **73**.

52

Knowing that he has just repulsed your attempt to take over his mind and knowing you to be defenceless, the left-hand image moves. It is the real King of the Elves, and he casts a spell of his own with a dramatic gesture. A luminous green halo pops forth from his fingertips. As it darts toward you the halo grows, and it encircles your waist before you can move. Your legs feel as if they have turned to jelly: you cannot stop yourself collapsing to the ground.

'Submit, mortal, I have defeated you,' cries the Elf King.

Will you submit? Turn to **255**. Or will you try to fight on? Turn to **272**.

53

Knowing what the Westermen plan for the Tree of Life, you determinedly hurry back to relay your information to the elves. Travelling along routes that seem to come unbidden to your mind, you reach a clearing that seems strangely familiar.

Your arrival is anticipated. An elf is waiting to return you to Elvenhame so you might hold a council of war. With a guide, you quickly make it to the fabulous home of these forest dwellers. Turn to **256**.

54

What is the dragon's name? Is it Gwelphstar (turn to **6**), Garoshtar (turn to **83**), Skardrig (turn to **93**), or Bethshebel (turn to **102**)?

55

A tall man and his short and stocky companion move apart to allow you room in front of the roaring log fire. Both give you a sidelong glance. They look rough weather-beaten men: the smaller of the two has a face like a bull-mastiff, the taller has the sly cunning look of a fox.

If you want to tell them who you are and why you have come to Burg, turn to **72**. If you wish to remain silent, turn to **94**.

56

You step back off the mound, which begins to shake as if there was an earthquake. The ground you have stepped back onto is quite firm, but even so you can feel the vibrations rocking you slightly.

The whole of the green hillock suddenly rolls upwards and away from you, leaving you standing on the edge of a ledge with a twenty-foot drop. As the hillock moves it creases and splits apart.

The dragon, for that is what the hillock really is, moves slowly as it wakes from its slumber. Turning its great scaly neck like a corkscrew, the ancient creature looks back over its shoulder at you. Its smouldering red eyes, as terrifying as the portals to hell, gaze at you from a craggy face the size of a cart.

Will you leap at its head to attack it before it is fully awake? If so, turn to **74**.

If you smile at it in the hope that it will not eat you, while preparing a spell if you know how, turn to **36**.

57

By the time you are directed to where the King of the Elves is preparing the defences, he is in position with his elven army in the trees around the Tree of Life itself.

The forest falls still. There are thousands of elves in the trees around the clearing but they make no sound. Even the animals and birds have fallen unnaturally silent. You look around and savour the beauty of this enchanted place, the fountain of all life. This may well be the last chance you ever have to revel in the natural glory of the Forest of Arden.

The sun breaks through the rolling clouds and bathes the clearing in brilliant light. The trumpets of the tree lilies swing round to greet the sun. You expect to hear the elves cheer at this good omen, but they remain grimly silent.

The oppressive din of the tramping of feet of thousands upon thousands of enemies grows inexorably closer. There is a crack like a firecracker as a tree is split and knocked to the ground by the passing of one of the great metallic monsters. Turn to **434**.

58

'A battle of wits?' The Elf King rises to this like a cat confronted with a helpless mouse. 'Very well, let us set an impossible task. He who fails to achieve the task has lost the contest.'

You are on the point of asserting that an impossible task by definition can never be achieved, but then you remember that elves abide by a contrary sort of logic. In any case, this is a test of your skill as a trickster. You nod your head. 'Agreed.'

The Elf King looks about him, then picks up a stone from the ground. Plucking a thread from the hem of his robe, he holds it between thumb and forefinger and says, 'Be rigid.' Instantly the thread straightens like a length of steel wire. 'Curl,' adds the Elf King, and now the thread twists into a corkscrew shape. Finally he says, 'Penetrate,' and drives the thread into the stone. It winds right through as easily as you might push a nail through a lump of butter. 'Return again to thread,' says the Elf King, and he holds the stone up dangling on the limp thread.

You take it from him. 'And what am I to do?'

'Withdraw the silk strand from the stone,' he says. 'Then thread it back through.'

'Easy enough.' You pull out the thread, then go over to a tree where you moisten the end with a drop of sticky sap. Next you find an ant crawling amid the leaf litter and glue the thread to its abdomen with the sap. As the ant wriggles, you lower it over the hole in the stone. It takes several attempts, but finally the ant crawls into the tiny hole. The Elf King glowers inscrutably as you hold up the stone and wait. Knowing that the ant is unable to turn around, it is only a matter of time before it emerges from the other end of the hole. You detach the ant and hand the stone back to the Elf King – once more with the silk neatly threaded through it.

He casts it aside. 'Another task—' he begins.

'Now it is my turn to set a task,' you protest. 'You have just set one.'

'That was by way of being an example of what was needed. Now we begin the contest proper.'

If you agree to attempt another task that he sets you, turn to **187**. If you think you might fail a second try, you will have to accept a more conventional duel: turn to **18**.

59

The dragon pins you to the ground beneath a huge claw. You look up from the massive green scaled claw to the beast's smouldering red eyes some thirty feet above. Clearly it wasn't as sleepy as you thought and your actions have made it think you were trying to kill it. The dragon opens its jaws wide and its stomach convulses. A second later a gout of poisonous gas and acid hits you like a suffocating and burning wave. There is no surviving the breath of an ancient green dragon.

60

The hairs on the nape of your neck begin to bristle as you step quietly between the Greenbark trees. You sense you are being watched.

You can hide (turn to **80**), stop and look about you (turn to **90**), or call out that you are Elanor's friend come in search of the immortal elves (turn to **109**).

61

You grab two flailing tentacles, haul yourself towards the creature's cone-shaped head and smash your fist repeatedly between its murky grey eyes. It coils loosen and fall away, and you break the surface gasping for air. Swimming to the far bank, you scramble out before the Embracer can recover. Turn to **13**.

62

The innkeeper's daughter is overjoyed to see her father returned. The innkeeper is as good as his word and he kills a fatted pig to give you a banquet fit for a king.

All too soon, however, you have to leave their pleasant hospitality behind and return to your quest. Yet you are already too late. As you journey back towards the Sirion river the Westermen have found the Tree of Life and cut it down. The forest is doomed and so, in the end, is all mankind. You have failed: the long winter is beginning.

63

Deciding your best chance of success in the duel is to use unarmed combat, you inform the King of the Elves of your choice. He scowls at you, then looks about him for a champion.

One of the few young elves walks forward. He is the only elf you have ever seen who you could describe as reasonably well built. His muscles are long and well defined. You have noticed how swift and deft the other elves are, and noted their surprising wiry strength. This young elf could prove to be a difficult adversary.

He walks forward, rocking up onto the balls of his feet, like a spring-heeled Jack, looks towards the king and asks, 'Do we fight to the death, lord? Have no fear for me.'

'You will duel until one of you submits or is killed,' answers the king. 'If you survive we have

two of the Lady of the Forest's potions to revive those who are wounded.'

Turning to you, he cautions, 'Don't make Gath-keri kill you, be sure to submit when he masters you.'

Gathkeri walks to one side of the grassy circle and waits confidently with his arms folded in front of him. He appears to be concentrating hard and mumbling.

Will you take up your position opposite Gathkeri? If so, turn to **201**. If you would rather try to get out of the duel by protesting to the king that you should be measured against your foes, the Westermen, not against the elves you have come to help, turn to **92**.

64

Speaking the word you clench your fist, imagining you are twisting and crushing the entrails of the Infernal Statue. The machine does not buckle or hold its stomach, as must a man affected by this puissant spell. Instead it lurches past the Tree of Life, then circles and lurches forward again, towards the deep blue pool.

The cries of the Westermen die to silence. In the resulting quiet you can hear muffled groans coming from somewhere inside the Infernal Statue. It totters on the brink of the pool and then begins to turn slowly back towards the Tree of Life. It seems to be recovering and will not be harmed by the spell again.

You can cast Bafflement (turn to **372**) or Tower of Will (turn to **207**).

65

Your sudden rush takes him by surprise as he was preparing a spell. Just before you reach him he calls out the word 'Sanctuary' in a ringing voice and claps his hands together. There is a second clap and he is gone. He has disappeared completely. You go to the door of the inn but there is no sign of him in the rain-lashed cobbled street.

Only the old woman in grey remains in the common room. She nods at you approvingly.

If you would like to sit at her table and talk with her, turn to **181**. If you wish to take a room in the inn for the night, turn to **333**.

66

You have taken a few more steps when the ground starts to shake. It feels like an earthquake and you fall down. Then the very ground beneath you hurtles skyward. There is a sudden hissing and a cloud of noisome vapours suddenly spurts from the other end of the hillock, giving the game away. You are lying on a dragon.

The dragon rolls over, away from the ledge it has been slumbering against, and as it does so you clamber up its back – an experience that is like scrambling up the side of a gigantic rolling barrel – and manage to grab hold of the bottle-green row of scales that runs in a crest down the creature's back.

Moving slowly as it wakes from its lengthy slumber, the dragon turns its neck like a corkscrew and points its cart-sized face at you. Its smouldering red eyes are like the gateways to hell.

Will you leap at its head to attack the dragon before it becomes fully awake? If so, turn to **74**. If you wish to smile at the dragon in the hope that it doesn't eat you, turn to **36**.

67

'The Westermen hate spiders. They say the spiders are ugly, poisonous and unnatural. To them spiders are the evil creatures of the Demoness. It does no harm to the forest to kill a spider. Are they right, these Westermen?'

If you say there is no harm in killing spiders, turn to **51**. If you say it is bad to kill spiders, turn to **106**.

If you have WILDERNESS LORE you can turn to **136**.

68

Pushing through the ferns you come to a desolate area of worn rock. The breeze carries the acrid smell of sulphurous gases. The few plants growing here are wizened and brown, struggling on the edge of survival. The strange gurgling sound starts again, further away. Then smoke rises out of the ground ahead of you followed by a watery burp.

If you wish to run away, turn to **32**. Otherwise, turn to **88**.

69

The Elf King raises his open hand in front of your face, palm upwards. It looks empty, but when he blows across it a flurry of fine ochre pollen flies into your eyes. Stumbling back, you wipe the pollen out of your eyes. It stings, causing tears to run down your face, and by the time your vision clears the elves have melted away into the forest depths. You are alone in the clearing. Turn to **78**.

70

If you have both the *Waterbearer* and *Bullhorn* code-words, turn to **256**. If you have only *Waterbearer*, turn to **42**. If you have neither codeword, or only *Bullhorn*, turn to **60**.

71

Your will invades the mind of the King of the Elves while he is still reeling from the effects of your Bafflement spell. As his senses return to him, you realize that his mind has been toughened beyond comprehension by the centuries of leading all elvendom, and the responsibility and judgment such a position requires. Quickly you grasp the moment to force him to speak the words of submission. You have won the duel. Turn to **263**.

72

You tell them of your quest to find the Tree of Knowledge in the Forest of Arden. The tallest of the two men introduces himself as Renard the Guide.

'If you seek the Tree of Knowledge, you will need a guide. The forest holds many snares, and its ways are treacherous. If you enter there alone you'll surely perish. That or you'll be hopelessly lost, never to see the lands of men again.'

'Ha!' snorts the short man. 'Renard doesn't know the whereabouts of this tree you seek, I'll warrant.'

'And what would a hunter know of the Tree of Knowledge?' snaps Renard.

The hunter turns away, quietly saying as his parting shot, 'About as much as you, Renard, and that's nothing at all.' He walks over to the kitchen door to talk to the young woman who pours him a jug of beer.

Renard sits down at at table, pulls up a second chair, and gestures you to join him.

If you ask him about the Tree of Knowledge, turn to **130**. If you want to learn about the other travellers in the inn, turn to **145**.

73

You stand up sharply when a thorn suddenly grows out of the branch on which you are sitting and pricks your bottom.

The appearance of the Lady in Grey changes. She is old again, as she appeared in the inn. She looks weary and downcast but resolute. 'If you do not quit the forest quickly the birds and beasts will see to it that you never return to the lands of men.'

You wander in the forest for many days. One day, you come across the bodies of hundreds of elves lying among the trees. It looks as though someone had just switched off their life force all at once – some even died in the middle of eating their supper. The forest is doomed and so are you.

74

It is a difficult leap, made harder by the dragon slowly rearing up onto its legs.

If you have AGILITY, turn to **86**.

Otherwise, you leap into the air but the dragon twitches its head away and you miss the target. With nothing to land on, you plummet twenty feet to the ground, landing almost underneath one of the creature's massive claws. Turn to **59**.

75

'The Westermen hate spiders. They say the spiders are ugly, poisonous and unnatural. To them spiders are the evil creatures of the Demoness. It does no harm to the forest to kill a spider. Are they right, these Westermen?'

If you say there is no harm in killing spiders, turn to **51**. If you say it is bad to kill spiders, turn to **89**.

76

Did you take up position in the circle on the west side, where the ground is flattest and where the wind is at your back, or the east side, where the ground is uneven and where the wind is in your face? If you have not done so, note on your Adventure Sheet which side of the circle you have chosen. Now turn to **110**.

77

Nothing in your life so far has prepared you for the first sight of the great Sirion river. The furthest bank – or perhaps it is just a large island in midstream – seems to be three miles away. Its roiling waters carry a multitude of dead tree branches towards the sea, like a vein carrying detritus out of a body.

Across the river the treeline is unbroken. You are deep in the rainforest now. The gigantic trees spread their branches more than a hundred feet from the ground here. At the river's edge mangroves reach far out into the water; bloated river buffalo shelter beneath their arching roots.

It is hard going here. At every other step you sink into oozing mud. Turn to **44**.

78

You trudge on, singling out and mentally marking individual trees as far away as you can see with the object of keeping them in sight so you don't walk in circles. Each time you reach your target tree you look back and try to identify the one you left behind so that you can choose another tree to make for in the same general direction. It is tiring work, and it exhausts you in body and mind.

As you walk on you eventually see gaunt grey crags jutting up out of the forest. It is a relief to find clear landmarks at last. The forest is broken here, as only grass can grow on where the soil is thin above the grey rock.

You walk out of the gloom into bright sunlight that hurts your eyes. There are countless paths leading back into the forest in all directions. As you stand contemplating which way to choose, a voice above and behind you says, 'Lost, are you?'

You turn round and look up. All you can see is a silver-feathered owl perched on top of an outcrop.

'Lost, are you?' the voice says again. It sounded as if the voice came from the owl but its beak didn't move.

If you have the emerald ring and the codeword *Crabclaw* on your Adventure Sheet, turn to **440**.

If you have the emerald ring and the codeword *Twinhead* on your Adventure Sheet, turn to **459**.

Otherwise, if you admit you are lost, turn to **258**. Or, you choose to ignore the voice and walk on, picking one of the many ways at random, turn to **277**.

79

The dragon seems to read your mind. The monster flicks its tail and licks its lips.

'Walk into the cavern and behold my hoard, which has been garnered from palaces across the whole world. Many of my treasures are old, so very old, that they have a tale to tell.'

The dragon bats you with a mighty claw, bowling you over so you fall to the ground. Once you have got back on your feet, the ancient creature ushers you forward into the dark cavern. Entering, you stop for a moment to adjust to the dim light. Blinking astonishment, your jaw goes slack at the sight before you. You stare in awe at the veritable mountain of golden coins, goblets, candelabra and jewellery that comprise the dragon's treasure trove.

'All the gold and jewels you can carry I give to you,' says the dragon.

At the creature's words, some of the coins fly up into air and push themselves against you. Soon you are covered in a golden crust which has gathered like barnacles do on the hull of a ship. Although your arms and legs are left free, you are terribly weighed down by the fortune that is now stuck to you. You try to prise the coins away but they are stuck fast by the magic of the dragon. Turn to **19**.

80

You hide underneath a clump of bushes for what seems an age. Here in the deepest part of the forest you can only guess that it is still daytime. When you are certain that you can hear and see nothing, you emerge from your hiding place and decide to journey on.

You have walked but half a mile further when the feeling of being watched returns.

If you wish to hide again, turn to **129**. If you would like to stop and look around you, turn to **90**. If you walk on, seemingly unaware, turn to **150**. Or you could try calling out that you are Elanor's friend come in search of the immortal elves: turn to **109**.

81

As the Embracer prepares to wrap you up in its tentacles, the smell of rot and marsh gas almost makes you gag. The tips of the fibrous tentacles wave in the air as if trying to sniff you out.

If you want to try to climb the great mass of vegetation and drive your sword point between its eyes, turn to **287**. Or you could slash at the other tentacles it is preparing to coil around you, so turn to **48**.

82

You speak the word and a magical silver shield appears to protect you from magic. But there is no one here using magic against you. You are wasting precious time. Now is your last chance to save the

Tree of Life.

You can cast Choking Fog (turn to **346**), Bafflement (turn to **113**), Visceral Disruption (turn to **64**), or Tower of Will (turn to **186**).

83

'Great Garoshtar, aid me now. Listen to and respect your friend's wishes – the forest needs your help.'

Garoshtar's great head rises slowly above you and his red eyes bore into yours.

'I need your help now, Garoshtar. The Westermen are marching to uproot the Tree of Life.'

The dragon is ready to bear you and to frighten the Westermen into the bargain. You ask him to attack the head of the Westermen columns as they advance, to give time for the King of the Elves to muster all his available forces. You climb onto Garoshtar's back and sit just in front of the great taut wings that beat the air like mainsails close-rigged in a storm.

You can remain astride Garoshtar's back while he attacks the Westermen (turn to **228**) or get him to deliver you to Elvenhame before making his attack (turn to **247**).

84

As the Westermen close in on you with swords and maces, you defend yourself as best you can while the Infernal Statue hews great lumps of green stained wood from the trunk of the Tree of Life. You fight like a hero, but for every foe you kill two more take his place. At the last your feet are knocked out from under you and your body is pierced by countless sword thrusts. You have failed the forest: it will be destroyed by the Westermen.

85

She will not listen as you ask her to stop and she moves so lightly you have a hard time keeping up.

'What have I done to upset you?' you ask. 'I can't help it if I don't know the ways of the forest as you do. I've had a hard life on the streets of Godorno. I didn't know what I would find here in the forest. Don't leave me here . . .'

Your pleas are useless: you cannot change her mind.

She flits between a curtain of creepers and down a secret tunnel, leaving you with an inexplicably strong feeling of loss. You try to find the concealed opening, but after hours of fruitless searching you reluctantly admit you have no choice but to follow your own destiny.

You wander in the forest for many days, until you come across the bodies of hundreds of elves lying among the trees. They are like figures of clay, cold and limp without the spark of life. You realize that the most terrible of fates has come to pass: the Westermen have succeeded in destroying the heart of the forest. You slump to your knees in despair as you hear their engines of destruction cutting through the trees towards you. Soon you will share the doom of the elves.

86

Your agile leap carries you into the monster's face, where you clutch at the beast's long thick whiskers to stop yourself falling off. You are right next to the dragon's mouth and your eyes are looking straight into its cavernous nostrils. But how will you take advantage of your precarious position?

If you consider your best move is to scramble up on top of the ancient creature's head, turn to **116**. Or will you daringly pat the dragon gently on the end of its great scaly nose? Turn to **125**.

87

A silver noose magically appears in the air before you and drops over your head. You try to drag the noose up and over your head, but the silvery cord tightens slowly until it flattens your windpipe. You grow purple owing to a lack of oxygen and the great effort you are putting into staying alive.

It is a futile struggle. Gurgling horribly, unable even to speak, you subside to the floor and black out, never to regain consciousness.

88

For a long while nothing happens. Nervously you begin to edge closer to the source of the strange sounds. There is a ledge ahead and you can't see what lies beyond.

There is a sudden dire hissing, as if a hundred vipers were baring their venomous fangs or perhaps it is an ancient dragon drawing breath. Then another great whoosh followed by an eruption of hot water that fountains into the air gives you the solution to the mystery. There is no dragon here and you are, indeed, nowhere near the Bonehill. Walking to the edge you see a cluster of large bubbling pools. All you have found is an area of hot springs. Every now and then a geyser erupts; the gurgling that follows is the escape of foul-smelling gases. There is nothing of interest here so you go on your way.

If you wish to turn and head west from here, turn to **43**. If you prefer to continue north in your original direction, turn to **127**.

89

'Why is it bad to kill spiders?' she asks.

If you say it is because all evil things as well as all good things must be tolerated in the forest, turn to **104**. If you believe it is because the birds would die without spiders to eat, and without birds to eat berries there would be no young trees, turn to **128**.

90

You stop still in your tracks and start to stare about, thinking to catch an elf slyly peeking at you from behind a tree.

There is the rushing whine of an arrow and a stabbing pain between your shoulder-blades. The force of the shot spins you round enabling you to see your assailant.

It is a tall, proud elf, who stands between two great Greenbark trees, his legs apart. He lets his bow fall to his side as your legs buckle under you. Your nameless attacker is a fine shot: his arrow has pierced your lung. Slowly you begin to drown in your own blood.

91

You marshal your thoughts and unleash the magic that begins a struggle of wills. Seconds after your eyes have glazed with the effort you realize your mistake. The centuries of being the one on whom all elvenkind has depended for leadership have hardened the king's will. He quickly exerts his power over your feeble mind. Your body trembles with the effort of trying to resist, but none the less you find yourself walking forward step by step until you are in front of the king. He compels you to kneel before him. Powerless to resist, you speak the words of submission. You have lost the duel. Turn to **163**.

92

'You would have us risk our lives in battle with a hundred thousand Westermen, yet you will not dare to face one elf in a duel? You are no better than the other humans.' The king's voice is loaded with contempt. 'We will have no dealings with you. Slay the coward.'

You begin to expostulate, but they are already drawing back on the bowstrings.

'All right, I'll fight the duel,' you cry. 'It won't prove anything, aahhh!' The first arrow pierces your windpipe – it is followed by many more. You die spurned by all elvendom.

93

You call out the dragon's name and its great head rears slowly above you and its eyes bore into yours. Its nostrils dilate as it sucks in a deep breath. Too late, you realize you lied to yourself about knowing the dragon's name. There is a terrible whooshing that sounds like the dragon's real name as it breathes acid and gas down on you. The intense burning and blistering that follows wracks your body with pain. Yet the torment is mercifully brief, as you quickly lapse into unconsciousness and then the permanent sleep of death.

94

Ignoring you, the two men continue their conversation about hunting in the forest. The shorter of the two becomes insulting when the taller claims to know the forest better than he.

'There are things in the forest which you wouldn't dare look upon, yet which I have seen with my own eyes.'

'What things?'

'Terrible things, green ghosts that walk through trees, phantasms and, in the darkest depths beyond the Sirion, a huge monster as big as a hill.'

'You've been too long alone in the forest. All your pent-up thoughts turn to babble.'

'I saw it, it blinked its great eye at me. An eye like a salver big enough to carry a boar's head.'

If you would like to tell them of your quest to the forest now, turn to **162**. Your eyes are now accustomed to the light and you can see the other travellers in the inn. If you would like to look them over before choosing a table, turn to **176**.

95

You jump nimbly and quietly over a stack of books and slink out between the chief's advisers. The guards at the porch don't notice you pass between them and you are soon safe back in the forest. The awful sights and sounds of the Westerman camp are soon far behind.

You can head west (turn to **43**), east (turn to **427**), south-west (turn to **70**), or south (turn to **78**).

96

Nothing in your life so far has prepared you for you first sight of the great Sirion river. The furthest bank – or perhaps it is just a large island in midstream – seems three miles away. Its roiling waters carry a multitude of dead tree branches towards the sea, like a vein carrying detritus out of a body.

Across the river the treeline is unbroken. You are deep in the rainforest now. The gigantic trees spread their branches more than a hundred feet from the ground here. At the river's edge mangroves reach far out into the water; bloated river buffalo shelter beneath their arching roots.

It is hard going here. At every other step you are sinking into oozing mud. Twice you nearly lose your life in the oozing mud: once when a vine you were clinging to snaps, and again when a huge river buffalo erupts out of the water between mangrove and rushes you. It storms through the water margin and crashes into the trees in hot pursuit. Soon the trees are too thick for it to follow and you trudge on, abandoning the river bank. Quite lost by now, you hope you can find a landmark to guide you. Turn to **131**.

97

The chief shakes his head. 'My new realm will never be safe until I have destroyed every last tree in the forest. Valerian tells me so and his counsel has always been good in the past.'

'But the whole world needs the forest,' you argue. 'Without the forest there would be no air to breathe. We will all die.'

'Valerian doesn't want to die any more than either you or I, I'll warrant. What nonsense is this you talk?' He narrows his eyes, suddenly suspicious. 'Where was it we met? Was it the Reaver's Inn in Bessaraban? Remind me.' He screws up his eyes in the effort of remembering a meeting that you know never took place.

If you pretend that you met in the Reaver's Inn in the far off city of Bessaraban, turn to **204**. If you make up an excuse and leave, turn to **305**.

98

The Lady of the Forest watches your departure sadly, but she does nothing to prevent you leaving. How can she be grieving at your loss when she hardly knows you? She must be mad. Nevertheless you quit her beautiful garden with regret and continue your quest for the Tree of Knowledge.

It will soon be Midsummer's Day. Where will you search for the tree next? You can head west (turn to **43**), east (turn to **427**), or south-west (turn to **70**).

99

You pass several of the great Umbellifer bushes, so called because of their bell shape. You walk on between them, where only grass that has been cropped by deer grows, until you come to an archway that has been cut through the thorns to provide a way into the shadowy recesses of the immense bush.

You can go inside the bush (turn to **119**), or hurry on past with not so much as a backward glance (turn to **127**.)

100

As you walk towards the guards you are horrified to see them spearing the animals that are fleeing the burning brush. The men throw the unfortunate beasts onto the fire beneath the great cauldron. The others laugh merrily as if they could think of no better sport than to wantonly slaughter helpless beasts.

You call a greeting above the hissing of the steam bellows that is rising and falling, driven by the metal machine. The guards stand up and fan out as if to surround you, without a word of command.

'Search the southerner for weapons,' shouts their captain.

If you surrender and let them search you, turn to **151**. If you try to fight your way out, turn to **202**.

101

Your spell of Bafflement crosses unseen the space that separates you and the King of the Elves, silently invading his mind. His eyes look at you, blankly uncomprehending, and the two false images that his magic created just flicker and die away. The king is powerless; he is far too confused to attempt a spell or even to move from the spot. Unfortunately he is also too baffled to realize the time has come for him to submit to you and acknowledge you the winner of the duel.

Under the rules of a duel you can only use magic to subdue him so you let the Bafflement fade and prepare another spell.

You can cast Visceral Disruption (turn to **111**) or Tower of Will (turn to **71**).

102

You call out the dragon's name. Its great head rears slowly above you and his glittering eyes bore into yours. His nostrils dilate as he sucks in a deep breath. Too late, you realize you were wrong about knowing the dragon's name. There is a terrible whooshing sound as the dragon's breath of acid and gas roars towards you. The torrent of gas and air rolls you across the ground and you are lucky to bang your head on a rock and spare yourself a more painful death. The forest is doomed.

103

It was a mistake to enter the forest without a guide. There is no time to do anything as the Embracer sucks you down into the murky depths. You struggle desperately hard but, unable to breathe, your strength soon fails you and you drown in the clutches of this hideous creature.

104

'The men who have come to the forest say that when the trees have been felled the undergrowth should be burned to clear it for humans to live in. They say burning returns all the goodness in the plants to the soil so that crops can flourish. Do you agree with them?' asks Elanor.

If you admit that you have no reason to disbelieve them, turn to **51**.

If you say instead that the forest should be kept as it is for it makes the air that man breathes, turn to **147**.

105

'So,' hisses your mirror image, 'you would rather shatter your promise . . .'

'You witless sprite,' you retort sharply, 'if I break the mirror right away, the enchantress will wake up. Be patient; I'll get around to it.'

'No!' wails the voice from the glass. 'You're lying. You intend to use me just as she has – but I'll foil that scheme. Wake, mistress, wake! A mortal prowls within your boudoir!'

Turn to **499**.

106

'Why is it bad to kill spiders?' she asks.

If you say it is because all evil things as well as all good things must be tolerated in the forest, turn to **51**. If you reason that without spiders to eat the birds would die, and without birds to eat berries there would be no young trees, turn to **128**.

107

'I have watched you coming here in the mirror I keep in my secret bower. I think you have the makings of a hero,' she says.

'Did it amuse you to watch me struggle to find my way in the forest?'

'Not at all. I was hoping you would survive at least this far.'

'That doesn't sound very encouraging.'

'Only you can shape your own destiny. I think perhaps you have greatness within you.'

'If you have plans for me why didn't you bring me straight here from the inn in Burg?'

'The ways of the forest cannot all be taught. They must be experienced. And besides, I needed to know your mettle.'

She smiles a smile that could mean anything from cruel amusement to genuine welcome; you are too confused by what she has said to judge the difference.

It feels slightly shaming to think that this woman has watched your most intimate moments in the forest. Still, you have done nothing to be ashamed of.

If you choose to go along with her, turn to **9**. If you are convinced she is mad and you wish to leave, turn to **98**.

108

You stride to the fireside and turn so that the light of the flaming logs plays across your face. All eyes are on you, but you can't see well in the gloom. The two men who had been rubbing their hands at the fire sit down at the other end of the old hall.

'We don't take kindly to strangers here. What brings you to Burg, southerner?'

It seems to be the sinister man cloaked in black who is talking. Do you tell him the truth, that you journey to the great Forest of Arden to seek the Tree of Knowledge (turn to **124**)? Or do you say that you are a scout sent out from your city to explore far-off lands and bring news back to your masters (turn to **154**)? If you have STREETWISE you can turn to **188**.

109

You call out loudly. 'I am a friend of Elanor, the Lady of the Forest. I come in search of the immortal elves.'

You feel rather unheroic, calling out like this when you don't know whether anyone can hear you. But there is also the nasty feeling that you might be struck by an arrow at any moment.

You call out a second time and this time, to your relief, you are answered. Turn to **120**.

110

You review the spells you can cast against the King of the Elves in the duel.

Vanish (**122**) allows you to disappear and move unseen. Choking Fog (**143**) brings a cloud of poisonous gas. Visceral Disruption (**347**) causes crippling stomach cramps. Shield of Defence (**326**) protects against manifest magical attacks. Bafflement (**347**) makes your foe unable to understand what is happening. Visions (**249**) creates two false illusions of yourself. Tower of Will (**174**) subdues your enemy and makes him do your will.

The elven bard announces the beginning of the duel. You are shocked at the swiftness of elven king's magic. Before you have even fully contemplated which spell to use, he cries a single word of power and vanishes. A moment later he reappears along with two exact copies of himself. You can't tell which is which because all three appear motionless.

You must quickly decide which spell to use first.

When you have done so turn to the paragraph indicated in brackets after the spell's name.

111

You mouth the strange words that set off Visceral Disruption. A spasm wracks the King of the Elves and he tries to stop himself clutching his stomach as the spell twists his guts.

You have never known anyone who could remain standing under the effects of this agonizing spell, but it is taking all of the Elf King's will. He cannot cast another spell.

'Cancel the spell, mortal. I concede victory to your sorcery,' the King of the Elves says from between clenched teeth.

Knowing how unpleasant the spell can be and out of compassion for the king, you quickly comply. You have won the duel. Turn to **263**.

112

'Do you think that the knowledge of the Tree of Life should be passed on to man so mankind can benefit from the tree's wisdom? Or are men too greedy and selfish to be trusted with this great wisdom?' she asks.

If you reply that wise men rule well and that you hope to take the wisdom of the Tree of Life back to the lands of men, turn to **104**. If you say that the knowledge must be guarded as a secret treasure and not given to men at large because man cannot be trusted, turn to **140**.

113

For a moment your Bafflement spell seems to have had little effect: the statue's sword arm rises and falls like a mindless piston. Soon, however, the sword starts to miss its mark, flailing pointlessly though the air. There are cries of alarm from the Westermen, who then begin to fall silent as the Infernal Statue lurches a few steps away from the tree and teeters near the edge of the deep blue pool.

It lapses into inaction – it would seem to be truly baffled. How will you follow up your success?

You can cast Visceral Disruption (turn to **362**), Choking Fog (turn to **31**), or Tower of Will (turn to **207**).

114

Your confident announcement fails to enthral the Elf King as you had hoped. Instead he only shakes his head slowly, the look in his eyes reflecting some inner emotion unknown to mortal men. Just as you open your mouth to try another guess, he comes striding rapidly forward to throw his cloak up in front of your eyes. There is no time to react before your vision is blotted out in a rustle of soft green fabric. A scent wafts to you, reminiscent of meadows and leafy lanes in summer.

Reaching up to pull aside the folds of the cloak, your fingers close only on a handful of fresh green leaves. You look around. The elves have vanished. You have no choice but to turn and trudge through the trees, calling out for them to return. But your pleas are unanswered except by the song of birds and the murmuring of a distant brook. Turn to **78**.

115

While you wait, quite still behind the chief's chair, you hear a visitor being announced. 'It is Valerian the Moon Druid, sire, he says he has important news. Shall we let him come in?'

'Aye, let him.' The speech of the Westermen is guttural and uncouth-sounding but you can understand their dialect.

It is the man you first saw in the inn at Burg. He is still dressed in a black travelling cloak but the hood is thrown back to reveal his hatchet-like face and pointed black goatee beard. He bows before the chief, then wrinkles his nose and stares at thin air in your general direction.

'I have driven off the tree bears, you will have no more trouble from them,' he tells the chief. He sniffs again and moves his head from side to side while fixing his gaze just above your head, giving him a most comical air.

The chief spreads out the map of the forest and his advisers gather round, almost blocking your exit. Will you try to get away now (turn to **29**) or wait to see what they may plan (turn to **4**)?

116

You nimbly climb up on top of the dragon's head, perching behind its glittering eyes. The monster reaches a claw up over its shoulder to flick you off onto the ground.

You can try to kill the dragon (turn to **135**), talk to it (turn to **178**), or hope that you can dodge the claw (turn to **133**).

117

It is a cold and blustery night. You look for another inn but there is none. The houses are shuttered and the doors barred. You try knocking but all your attempts at seeking entry are ignored. The inhabitants really don't like strangers here.

A woman shouts from a top window, 'You'd best get outside the gates before they turn the dogs loose in the streets.'

As she speaks you hear the baying of a pack of dogs from near the gate. You walk quickly through. The dog handlers seem to be sizing you up as quarry as they shut the gate behind you.

You pass a cold, damp night outside the town, awakening stiff and soaked through in morning. You are only too glad to leave Burg behind you. Turn to **210**.

118

There is a tingling pins-and-needles feeling as the sprite's magic takes effect. If you are currently below your initial Life Points score, restore it to normal. If you are as yet uninjured, you gain 1 Life Point permanently – for instance, an initial score of 10 would now be changed to 11 on your Adventure Sheet.

'Now do as you promised,' urges the sprite in the mirror. 'Free me.'

If you break the mirror, turn to **418**. If not, turn to **105**.

119

The archway leads into a tunnel that has been cut through the thick branches and thorns of the bell-shaped bush. You walk on towards the great open space that surrounds the trunk of the bush.

Looking back, however, you cannot make out the archway at all, even though it should be directly behind you. You press on anyway until you hear a chirruping little voice say, 'Welcome, sirrah, 'tis a pretty place to spend the rest of your days, is it not?'

A strange little man the size of a small capuchin monkey sits cross-legged on a giant toadstool. Even in the dim light you can see the fungus is liver-spotted and looks poisonous.

'Come, share my provender,' invites the little man as he breaks off a piece of the toadstool on which he is sitting. He offers it to you. 'Share my provender, there is nothing more helpful to a hero

than the flesh of the Blood of Iron toadstool.' The little imp proffers it to you with an elaborate bow.

If you take and eat the flesh, turn to **138**. If you want to try to kill the little man, turn to **148**. If you ask him to help you in your quest, turn to **158**.

120

You are surrounded by a circle of elves, all of whom seem to have appeared as if by magic. They look solemn but not hostile. Their faces have the perfect beauty of unsullied youth but their green almond-shaped eyes are like windows onto the wisdom of the centuries. Their skin is flawless pale green with a silvery bloom like grape bloom. Their long straight hair is the colour of rich red wine. They seem not in

the least surprised to see you.

You wait for them to say something but they seem in no hurry, so you tell them you are a friend of the forest and an enemy of the burners. Turn to **180**.

121

Seeing your eyes measuring the left of the three images, the one you are looking at smiles imperturbably, but something tells you, you have guessed correctly.

Will you now cast Bafflement (turn to **101**), Visceral Disruption (turn to **111**), or Tower of Will (turn to **91**)?

122

You cry a single word of power and vanish, then move slowly and silently in a circle to your right while you prepare another spell.

As you creep silently along, you notice to your dismay the faces of all the elves turned towards you. Several are grinning. The King of the Elves is looking straight at you as he mouths another incantation.

Your legs feel as if they have turned to jelly and you cannot stop yourself collapsing to the ground.

'Submit, mortal, I have defeated you,' cries the King of the Elves.

If you do as he requests, turn to **255**. If you try to fight on, turn to **272**.

123

The King of the Elves draws a green silk veil from his waist, holds it up and lets it fall from in front of his eyes.

'See your peril, mortal, and despair.'

His words ring out as though your skull was a vast hollow chamber and the elf was exhorting you from within it, his words rolling through your senses like ocean waves. As the veil falls it is as if scales had dropped from your eyes. You see the forest for what it is, a hostile place, inimical to man. Everything around you is united against your intrusion. The plants will snare you and tear you limb from limb, with the slow strength of growth. The ants will eat you alive. Stinging insects will plague you and bears

will maul you. You do indeed despair at the awful
nature of your plight. Losing reason you flee in fear.
As the veil falls lightly to the ground, so the terror
passes and you stop.

'You have stepped outside the circle, mortal, and
forfeited the duel. I am the victor,' says the king.

His magic made you break the rules and lose.
Turn to **163**.

124

'It is my intention to search for the Tree of Knowledge in the Forest of Arden,' you announce in a firm
clear voice.

As your eyes become accustomed to the gloom
you can begin to make out details of those in the
room. The black-cowled man merely stares inscrutably. A woman, old and weather-beaten, in a grey
robe, looks up at you with interest. The two who
were at the fire stand up and walk over to you. The
shorter one has a face that reminds you of a bull-
mastiff. 'Why would you seek the Tree of Knowledge?' he asks. 'What use is it to you, a southerner?'

'Fool, don't speak to him of the tree,' interrupts
the man in black. 'All must be left as it is, nothing
changed. The knowledge of the tree is lost to men
and it is better that way.'

The woman speaks with a clear voice that sounds
too young for her age. 'You would have it that way.
You are not at one with the forest. Because the tree
sees your evil heart, you seek to keep its knowledge
and pervert it.'

'You dare to say I am no friend of the forest?' The black cowled man surges to his feet and the cowl slips back to reveal a bald head, a hatchet-thin face with a long black goatee beard and eyes of flint.

'You lost your way in the forest many years ago.'

'I didn't need you to find me, old woman. You only dare challenge me now because you think these simple folk of Burg can offer you protection.'

'You know full well I am at my strongest in the forest, Valerian,' says the woman. 'The beasts follow me. They sense your evil.'

'There is a new power astir in the forest,' he retorts. 'It will sweep you and all your bestial followers aside like chaff in the wind.'

'There is no cause to fill the hearts of the good people of Burg with dismay. I know of what you speak . . .'

He sneers. 'Much good may the knowledge do you, old one. Haven't you heard the song of the wind? The time of man has come to the forest. All must change – or pass away.'

Valerian speaks the last words in such dire tones that three townsfolk at the nearby table hastily leave the inn. Valerian himself twitches his cloak around him and follows them out, pausing to give you a last look as though committing your face to memory.

If you can take a room at the inn for the night, turn to **333**. Or you can talk to some of the inn's inhabitants: choose between the hunter and the guide who are by the fire (turn to **297**) and the woman in grey (turn to **181**).

125

Your patting makes the dragon wrinkle up its nose, and there is a roar as it starts to sneeze. Its breath is a mixture of acid and poisonous gas. It hits you like a wave of blistering, burning pain. There is no surviving the breath of an ancient green dragon.

126

You shake your head. 'Better that I retain it for now. If we are to be allies, what better token that I fight for the elves than that their king has entrusted me with his royal symbol?'

He knows you have guessed him aright. If you had returned the ring, the elves would no doubt have found some way to back out of their bargain. Now they are bound to fight beside you, and your carefully chosen words allow the king to accede to this without losing his dignity. His eyes show a flicker of grudging admiration as he says, 'Well spoken, mortal. Now let us feast and discuss our plans.'

Note the Elf King's ring among your possessions, then turn to **232**.

127

A chameleon on a tree changes colour to pale yellow as you walk past it. A beautiful silken-winged butterfly, black and scarlet, settles on your shoulder and spreads its wings in the sun. You are beginning to feel harmony with the forest at last. You journey on, hopeful and determined. Turn to **277**.

128

'Abide with me here a while,' Elanor requests. 'I can teach you something about the forest and its ways. And I can put you to the test again, to see if you are worthy of being hailed the saviour of the forest.'

You spend three days in the tree-house and the meadow-garden talking with Elanor about the forest she loves. You had never realized how much all living things are linked, each depending on the others for survival.

The forest, you learn, is teeming with an abundant wealth of life. All things are tolerated in the forest, which is neither a good nor an evil region, as long as they do not threaten the balance of nature.

After you have partaken of a delicious repast of mushrooms and loganberries on the third day, Elanor starts to question you again, to see if you have learned anything. Turn to **112**.

129

This time you hide beneath the roots of a fallen pine tree. You try to stay calm to still the pounding of your heart that makes the blood rush loudly in your ears. This time you think you may have heard cruel-sounding laughter, now off to one side, now behind you, and now off to another side. You see nothing so at last you decide to journey on.

You have walked but half a mile further when the you stumble against a branch. The deep green of the forest by day is giving way to the blackest dark of the forest by night. You will never find the elves on

Midsummer's Day now. You will have to find a place to rest and hope the elves will still receive you cordially at a later date. Turn to **139**.

130

'The Tree of Knowledge grows alone out of a blue pool in the very centre of the forest. It is an ancient Greenbark tree with gold and silver leaves which are said never to fall.'

'Have you seen it?' you ask Renard.

'Once from a long way off. But I didn't dare talk to it.'

'It can talk? Is there anyone here in Burg who has spoken with the tree?' you ask, glancing at the other travellers in the inn.

'No, no. The folk here are simple enough. Ask them about the tree and they'll likely make something up just to satisfy your asking. Now look, why don't you put up for the night at my house and we can set out at first light?'

Renard seems keen to take you away from the inn. Looking around you notice the old woman in grey seems to be taking an interest in you.

If you go with Renard to his house, turn to **224**.
If you would rather stay and talk to the travellers in the inn a while longer, turn to **176**.

131

The path twists and turns, winding through dense undergrowth overhung by barrel-like Gwelph trees that are festooned with lianas. You try to fix the shape of each tree in your mind so you will know if you have passed one before. The thin crooked branches that sprout from the top of the barrel-like boles remind you of terrified old men with their hair standing on end.

To your dismay the path ends in a little clearing choked with dead leaves with two paths leading off in different directions. Each is lined with thorn bushes that have grown to the height of a man and are covered in inch-long purple barbs which ooze an orange fluid. The thorns would break off in your flesh if you brushed against them.

You can take the left-hand path (turn to **196**) or the right-hand path (turn to **211**).

If you despair of ever finding your way out of the forest, turn to **156**. If you wish to mark one of the great Gwelph trees by scraping away a patch of bark, turn to **177**.

132

You have directed your spell against one of the king's images, not against the king himself. The image you have assailed disappears with a startling pop, but the elf has used the time he has gained to prepare another spell.

The King of the Elves draws a green silk veil from his waist and lets it fall from in front of his eyes.

'See your peril, mortal, and despair.'

His words ring out as though your skull was a vast hollow chamber and the elf was exhorting you from within it, his words echoing through your senses. As the veil falls it is as if scales had dropped from your eyes. You see the forest for what it is, a hostile place, inimical to man. Everything around you is united against your intrusion. The plants will snare you and tear you limb from limb with the slow strength of their growth. The ants will eat you alive. Stinging insects will plague you and bears will maul you. You do indeed despair at the awful nature of your plight.

Losing reason you flee in fear. As the veil falls lightly to the ground, so the terror passes and you stop.

'You have stepped outside the circle, mortal, and forfeited the duel. I am the victor,' says the king.

His magic made you break the rules and lose. Turn to **163**.

133

The great claw sweeps you clean off the monster's head. The only way to dodge would have been to jump to your death in any case. You fall stunned on the ground and the dragon pins you to the earth beneath a massive claw. You look from the green scaled claw to the smouldering red eyes thirty feet above. It thinks you were trying to kill it. The dragon opens it jaws wide and its stomach convulses. A second later a gout of poisonous gas and acid hits you like a wave. There is no surviving the breath of an ancient green dragon.

134

Watching from the edge of the trees you see a man who bears an uncanny resemblance to the girl in the inn at Burg. He must be her father.

If you wish to free him from the clutches of the Westermen, turn to **264**. If you are content to abandon him to their tender mercies, turn to **279**.

135

You are too slow. The great claw sweeps you clean off the monster's head. You fall stunned to the ground; the dragon pins you there beneath the other massive claw. You look from the huge green scaled claw to the smouldering red eyes thirty feet above. The dragon opens its jaws wide and its stomach convulses. A second later a gout of poisonous gas and acid hit you like a wave. There is no surviving the breath of an ancient green dragon.

136

Your knowledge of the wilderness and the complicated web of links between all the living things in the forest makes this an easy question to answer.

'Without spiders to eat, the birds would die and without birds to eat berries and spread seeds there would be no young trees,' you say confidently. 'Without young trees to replace the old fallen hulks there would be no forest.' Turn to **128**.

137

If you have CUNNING and want to challenge the Elf King to a battle of wits, turn to **58**.

If you have ARCHERY and a longbow, you can propose a contest to prove the better bowman; turn to **159**.

Otherwise, you hesitate and the elves themselves choose the terms of the duel: turn to **18**.

138

The toadstool is a dull red colour, spotted with purple. Underneath the soft gills are mauve. You ask nervously whether it is poisonous.

'No, no, never, not poisonous, my dear, Oh no! The Kwerrel eats it every day.'

It tastes surprisingly good; it almost melts in your mouth.

Quite soon, however, you begin to feel sleepy. You walk a few steps further then sit down with your back to the central trunk of the giant bush. Feeling warm, snug and content you fall into a deep sleep. Turn to **189**.

139

The next day you awake feeling uneasy and begin your journey once more. The feeling of being watched soon returns. There seems to be no point in hiding; there might not be anything there. You call out that you have come to search for the immortal elves.

A soft high voice, but a cold voice none the less,

speaks with a total lack of emotion. 'It is not the day to seek a meeting with the elves.'

You spin round to find the source of the words. There is the rushing whine of an arrow and a stabbing pain between your shoulder-blades.

The force of the shot spins you round and you see your killer: a tall, proud elf, standing braced with feet apart between two great Greenbark trees. He lets his bow fall to his side in a gesture of merciless contempt.

The arrow has pierced your lung and you begin to drown in your own blood. The elf looks on without pity as you die.

140

'You pass the test. I know you to be of true heart. You care about living things. You are the saviour of the forest. I will do all in my power to aid you, but you will need the elves on your side. They are the real masters of the forest.'

Elanor fills two horn cups of elderflower nectar and offers you one. Taking the drink, you raise the cup in thanks before putting it to your lips. The nectar is marvellously refreshing, sweet but not cloying to the taste.

'The Westermen have cut great swathes through the forest. They are settling the land, but without the trees the soil will be carried away by the wind and this region will become a terrible desert. These men don't know what they are doing, and they care nothing for life. You must stop them.'

'How am I to stop them?' you ask. 'How strong are they?'

'Tens of thousands. They came from the western plains like columns of ants and devoured everything in their path.'

Turn to **152**.

141

The red liquid tastes vile, but unlike medicine it doesn't seem to do anything to you. You start to run as the swarm of bees settles around your head, but you have left it too late. Death from a hundred bee stings is not a pleasant way to leave the world. Your neck swells until your windpipe closes right up, and slowly but surely you choke to death. You bitterly rue your folly in upsetting Elanor, the Lady of the Forest, and you have paid the price.

142

This time your rush makes Gathkeri stumble back over a hummock and your lunge catches him. You start to wrestle, trying to throw him to the ground.

For your next manoeuvre, you can try to throttle your opponent (turn to **435**) or try to throw him to the ground so that you land on top of him (turn to **425**).

143

Throwing your arms wide to embrace the wind and blowing mightily as if playing a trumpet you cast the mighty spell Choking Fog. There is a hiss and a puff of green smoke appears in front of the three images of your foe, one of which you know to be real.

Look at your Adventure Sheet to see whether you stated you are standing with the wind at your back or the wind at your face. If you are standing with the wind at your back, turn to **285**. If you are standing with the wind on your face, turn to **294**.

144

You back off and reach a rock behind which you can take cover.

The Infernal Statue recovers its equilibrium and hacks into the trunk of the Tree of Life once more. The sword bites deep and one of the tree's great branches cracks and falls to the ground, killing and maiming more than twenty of its assailants. At the next sword blow another branch cracks and falls, and those not dead or trapped fall back as the machine completes its job of destruction.

You screw up your courage and rush once more against the machine but you are too late. One last great blow splits the trunk in the middle and the tree is dead. The destruction of the Tree of Life shatters your hopes. Utterly dejected you do not resist as the Westermen take you prisoner. The only certainty about the future is that you will be a slave of the forces that you should have defeated.

145

'There's Marek the Hunter there.' He points to the stocky man with a face like a bull-mastiff, drinking beer by the kitchen door. 'He's a good enough man if it's simple hunting you're after.' Renard looks at you as if you must be after something more.

'Then there's old Oakmother there, lives in the forest. She says she comes to Burg just to remind herself once in a while that she is a human being. She's a strange old cove.' He points to a weather-beaten old woman in a grey robe. 'She won't eat meat. Says her friends the animals will desert her if he does. Says they'll smell it on her skin.' Renard shakes his head pityingly.

'And who is the man in black?' you whisper.

'I am Valerian and I have the ears of a bat, the eyes of an owl and the sting of a viper.' The man in black gets to his feet and approaches.

Renard slinks away to join Marek the Hunter. Turn to **252**.

146

The chief looks at you as though scales have fallen from his eyes. 'Miserable trickster . . . Hmm, you look strong and fit, a fine log-puller you'll make.'

Valerian takes away your wand, and the guards strip you of your possessions. Without even asking who you are or where you have come from they chain you to a yoke beside another slave.

You begin a life of back-breaking work, pulling tree trunks from the fellers to the sawyers for week after week, year after year. Your pitiful existence is dominated by thoughts of how you might make a desperate escape before the toil kills you.

147

'Hunters come to the forest from Burg, Dale and the few villages near the forest's edge. They come to kill and then to eat and to find furs to wear. Should I stop them coming to the forest? It lies within my power.'

If you reply that the hunters should be stopped, turn to **51**. If you reply that the hunters are so few that it cannot harm the forest, turn to **140**.

148

As soon as the idea of killing the impish little man forms in your head, he bounds down from the toadstool.

'It's mischief you're planning, is it? May your bones rot to feed the Umbellifer bush. I leave you its prisoner.'

With that he rushes to the central trunk of the giant bush and scrambles up just as if he was a monkey, writhing sinuously past the wicked barbed thorns. You could never follow such a difficult route. The little imp is soon lost to sight and you start to look for a way out of the bush. Turn to **432**.

149

You have directed your spell against one of the king's images, not against the king himself. The image you have assailed disappears with a startling pop but the elf has used this time to prepare another spell.

The King of the Elves draws a green silk veil from his waist and lets it fall from in front of his eyes.

'See your peril, mortal, and despair.'

His words ring out as though your skull was a vast hollow chamber and the elf was exhorting you from within it, his words echoing through your senses. As the veil falls it is as if scales had dropped from your eyes. You see the forest for what it is, a hostile place, inimical to man. Everything around you is united against your intrusion. The plants will snare you and tear you limb and limb with the slow strength of growth. The ants will eat you alive. Stinging insects will plague you and ears will maul you. You do indeed despair at the awful nature of your plight.

Losing reason you flee in fear. As the veil falls lightly to the ground, so the terror passes and you stop.

'You have stepped outside the circle, mortal, and forfeited the duel. I am the victor,' declares the king.

His magic has made you break the rules. You have lost. Turn to **163**.

150

You feign nonchalance as you walk on between the beautiful Greenbark trees, which every now and then let a golden leaf fall on your brow. Though you have been hit by several leaves you never see one falling. It is as if the gargantuan trees, with their trunks as wide as towers, have been shaken slightly by your footsteps.

A little way ahead there is a clearing from which you can hear the crackle of fire and see the orange flickering of flame. The sun must have set fire to the dried grass. Advancing closer, you see a chipmunk chittering in panic inside the closing ring of flames. A solid wall of fire surrounds the desperate little animal, a fire so strong that it would undoubtedly burn you horribly.

If you brave the flames to save the chipmunk, turn to **160**. If you keep out of the clearing on the grounds that you will make an easy target there, turn to **170**.

151

You surrender yourself up to the Westermen guards and are taken before a man who is clearly their chief.

The Chief of the Westermen is a balding corpulent man whose eyes seem to gleam with greed. He appraises your worth in a quick glance. 'Hmm, you look – strong and fit – doubtless you'll make a fine log-puller.'

Without even asking who you are or where you have come from the Westermen chain you to a yoke beside a man who reminds you of the girl in the inn at Burg. It must be her father.

If you have SPELLS, turn to **229**. Otherwise you begin a life of back-breaking work, pulling tree trunks from the fellers to the sawyers for week after week, year after year. Your pitiful existence is dominated by thoughts of how you might make a desperate escape before the toil kills you. There is no escape. You live only to see the utter destruction of the Forest of Arden.

152

'But how am I to stop them? I am a stranger here in the forest.'

'Make the elves fight them. Kill the Westermen's leader. Wake the mighty dragon and send him forth to destroy them. If the forest perishes the whole world will die.'

'Which of these three should I do?' you ask. 'Or is not as simple as that, and I must do two or even all three of these things?'

'I do not know.'

'Can't you talk to the elves?'

'The elves will talk to men only on Midsummer's Day. On that day, you must find them and convince them to help you save the forest. I can never talk with elvenkind except on Midsummer's Day.'

There are so many questions you would like to ask Elanor, but the elderflower nectar seems to be going to your head and you feel too drowsy to continue.

'Sleep now, and awake a hero.'

As Elanor says the word sleep, your eyes shut and you sink gently down on the straw mattress, already deep in slumber. Turn to **166**.

153

Renard thanks you for the six pieces of gold; delete them from the money recorded on your Adventure Sheet. 'It's not that I'm a coward, you understand. It's just that nobody in their right mind would brave the Bonehill.'

You awake at dawn in time to glimpse Renard's disappearing back. It seems he doesn't want to stay a moment longer than he has to. You slept soundly and feel invigorated and confident as you begin to climb the slope away from the Sirion river.

You may restore up to 2 lost Life Points. Turn to **237**.

154

'Then tell your masters that Burg is a broken-down little hamlet soon to be swamped by the forest. Go and tell them there is nothing for them here.'

The man in black steps forward. You can see a hatchet-shaped face inside the cowl of his robe and a pointed black goatee beard. He is flanked by the two who were by the fire.

'We don't take to foreigners. You better leave Burg before we set the dogs on you.'

It seems they think you are a spy sent out to find rich towns to pillage and despoil. You decide to leave while you can still walk. Turn to **117**.

155

You grab the phial and gulp down the cloudy blue fluid. The owl, perched on a tree, watches as unblinking as ever.

'You have just drunk the mulch of the fire lizard's gizzard. You have not long to live.'

The owl is right. Your throat goes into spasm as the poison starts to work and soon you cannot breathe. You fall to the ground writhing in agony, but it is not long before unconsciousness brings merciful release from the pain of the poison.

156

All is not lost if you have WILDERNESS LORE, in which case turn to **251**. Otherwise, crushed by despair you realize you will never find your way out of the forest. There is nothing you can eat here – everything tastes of poison, even the dead leaves. You try eating some of the earwigs in the leaf litter but their blood burns your mouth like acid.

Beyond caring, you push your way into the undergrowth, heedless of the purple thorns that rip your flesh. The bushes are not as thick as you believed. You crash through into a dark avenue between tall slender trees growing so close together you cannot force your way between their trunks. Resigned to your fate you walk on down the avenue for what seems an age.

You start to pass bodies lying where they have fallen, one at a time, and then a forlorn-looking little group, huddled together. Exhausted and starving like the others before, you give up hope and lie down to die.

157

Squirming quickly round to the statue's back you work at the screws. Two come free and the head starts to tilt. With one great forearm smash you knock it off and the Infernal Statue lurches back from the Tree of Life. Inside the machine is a small man who cannot defend himself. You rain blows down on his head and he slumps forward, knocking the strange levers inside the machine and sending it striding towards the deep blue pool.

It totters on the brink of the pool and you leap clear just as it keels over into the water. There is a rush of steam like a geyser, followed by an explosion underwater as the machine tears itself apart. The

Westermen cry out in alarm and begin to retreat, harried by the arrows of the elves.

Turn to **500**.

158

'You want my help, what is in it for me then? How will you pay your side of the bargain?'

If you offer the little imp gold, turn to **214**. If you beg him to help you for the sake of the forest and all who dwell there, turn to **225**. If you have it, you can offer him the Lady of the Forest's emerald ring: turn to **236**. Or you can offer him a magic potion, if you are carrying one: turn to **243**.

159

A slender elf with moon-coloured hair steps forward to answer his monarch's summons. He carries a bow of silver-chased ivory, and the fletching of the arrows in his quiver is purest white. 'Your opponent will be Hundranas,' the Elf King tells you. He points to a tall tree. 'That branch will be the target.'

You look where he is pointing, then glance back at him. 'Which branch?'

'The one where the orchid grows.'

You look back. You had not noticed before the flower blazing like a pale jewel against the black bark of the tree. Hundranas gestures for you to take the first shot. You nock on an arrow and send it sailing up towards the branch. It strikes wide of the orchid, but it was only intended as a ranging shot. At least now you have a good sense of the allowance you need to make for height and wind speed.

Huldranas' arrow flashes from his bow. It impales one of the petals of the orchid. He turns to you with a casual look that betrays neither arrogance nor tension. Again without a word, he gestures for you to shoot.

As you sight along your arrow, you consider what to do. You could go for a cautious shot, since Huldranas' first arrow might have been lucky (turn to **320**). Or you could attempt a shot slightly better than his, perhaps striking the orchid in its centre (turn to **469**). Or will you try an extremely difficult but impressive shot, such as shooting through the thin twig at the end of the branch (turn to **276**)?

160

As soon as you make the jump to clear the ring of flame, the fire vanishes without even a trace of smoke. The chipmunk too has vanished. Instead you are surrounded by a circle of elves who have appeared as if by magic.

The elves look solemn but not hostile. Their faces have the perfect beauty of unsullied youth, but their green almond eyes are like windows that open to the wisdom of the centuries. Their skin is flawless pale green with a silvery dusting like grape bloom. Their long straight hair is the colour of rich red wine.

They seem not in the least surprised to see you. You wait for them to say something but they seem in no hurry, so you tell them you are a friend of the forest and an enemy of the burners. Turn to **180**.

161

Gathkeri closes in, still circling but moving ever closer, until he suddenly launches into a flurry of kicks aimed at your head. You parry them with your arms up high and step to the right, watching his movements, learning so that you can anticipate what he will do. Now that you have assessed his fighting style you can see that he uses kicks better than he punches, and deduce that he might not be able to fight so well at close quarters. Armed with this knowledge you can probably beat him.

You can try to grapple him (turn to **183**) or attack him with your fists and feet (turn to **172**).

162

You tell them of your quest to find the Tree of Knowledge in the Forest of Arden, after which the taller of the two introduces himself as Renard the Guide.

'You will need a guide in the forest, or you'll be lost, never to see the lands of men again.'

'Renard doesn't know the whereabouts of this tree you seek, I'll warrant,' comments Marek.

'What would a hunter know of the Tree of Knowledge?'

The hunter turns away; his parting shot is: 'About as much as you, Renard, and that is nothing at all.' He walks over to the kitchen door to talk to the young woman, who pours him a jug of beer.

Renard sits down at a table, draws up a second chair and gestures for you to join him.

If you wish to ask him about the Tree of Knowledge, turn to **130**. If you wish to learn more about the other travellers, turn to **145**. Or will you ask the hunter about the monster he says he has seen? Turn to **281**.

163

To your shame you have lost the duel and failed the elven test. The elves vanish back into the forest, warning you to return straight to Burg or you will suffer a death of a thousand bites and stings here in the forest. Turn to **384**.

164

The ants inject poison with every bite. You take more than a hundred bites as you toil uphill, at last abandoning flight and stripping off your gear in a final effort to scrape the ants from your skin.

It is too late: the venom weakens your muscles and you sink helpless to the forest floor, mercifully losing consciousness before the ants consume you. Within minutes they strip your flesh to the bone. It does not do to have the whole forest against you.

165

Turning your back on a dragon is never wise. The ancient creature pins you to the ground beneath a huge claw. You look up from the massive green scaled claw to the smouldering red eyes thirty feet above. It wasn't as sleepy as you thought and now it thinks you were trying to kill it. The dragon opens its jaws wide and its stomach convulses. A second later a gout of poisonous gas and acid hit you like a wave. There is no surviving the breath of an ancient green dragon.

166

When you awake you are wonderfully restored to healty vitality: restore any Life Points you have lost.

Elanor is nowhere to be seen. On the third finger of your right hand, however, is an emerald ring with the stone set in a furled silver leaf. It fits perfectly. You get up, stretch your limbs, and, deep in thought, rub the gem.

You feel in your bones that it is your destiny to save the forest and that you will risk your life to do so. You suffer a moment's unease as you worry about the dangers ahead, an unease that turns to deep-rooted fear. Once more you look at the ring. Is it magical? Is it the ring causing you to feel the reckless courage of a hero? Or did the blood of a hero always run in your veins?

Note the emerald ring among the possessions listed on your Adventure Sheet.

If you wish to take off the ring, turn to **179**. If you trust Elanor and leave the ring on, turn to **35**.

167

Renard surlily agrees to take you up the Bonehill on the morrow, and you settle down to sleep, exhausted after days of hard travelling.

At dawn, when you awake, Renard is nowhere to

be seen and neither is your money pouch. He must have stolen it while you slept before slinking away into the forest. You will never find him. He has left you penniless, but at least he didn't slit your throat.

You slept soundly enough but the loss of your money has upset you, even though you can foresee no need for money here in the forest. Strike any money you may have been carrying off your Adventure Sheet.

Cursing Renard, you begin to climb the slope away from the Sirion river. Turn to **237**.

168

The black tarry goo smells of putrefaction and does not deter the bees at all. You start to run as the swarm of bees settles around your head, but you have left it too late. Death from a hundred bee stings is not pleasant. Your neck swells until your windpipe is closed right up and you choke to death. You rue bitterly your folly in upsetting Elanor, the Lady of the Forest, and you have paid the price.

169

You cast your best attack spell for this situation: a magical javelin that should always find its mark. It appears in your right hand just as a silver noose materializes in the air before you. You hurl the javelin, which leaves a trail of golden sparks in the air, as the silver noose rises above you and drops towards your head.

Before the noose can tighten around your neck

and as the javelin flies towards him, Valerian speaks a word of negation: both his spell and yours are cancelled. The golden javelin and the silver noose disappear.

'Had I known you were a sorcerer I should not have been so short with you. A sorcerer is by nature secretive. We need not prolong our quarrel here.' Valerian sits down again at his table.

If you attack him with another spell, turn to **206**. If you want to talk to the woman in grey, who seems unmoved by the violence she has seen, turn to **181**.

170

You turn your back on the chittering chipmunk, leaving it to a fiery death. But you have taken no more than three steps before you hear the rushing whine of an arrow as it heads towards you.

You attempt to dodge the unseen attack, but your action is in vain. There is a terrible stabbing pain in middle of your back and you are knocked to your knees by the force of the shot. Looking down, you see the sharp head of a deadly elven arrow protruding from your belly; your stomach convulses and you begin to cough up blood.

Out of the corner of one eye you can see your assailant: a tall, proud elf, who is standing between two greet Greenbark trees. An arrow is already nocked ready for a second shot, but it proves unnecessary as the first has done its work. As your lifeblood spills onto the ground, the silent elf looks on without pity.

171

Your knowledge of the wilderness and the ways of even its smallest creatures makes this an easy question to answer. You know full well that without ants to clear away the debris of wood and leaves the forest would drown in a blanket of rot in but a few years. Turn to **67**.

172

You close with Gathkeri and unleash a combination of kicks and punches. The elf, however, is quicker than you. At the end of the exchange of blows his foot smashes into your chest at the bottom of your ribcage, causing you to double up in pain. Gathkeri has smashed some of your ribs: lose 5 Life Points.

The elf gives you no time to recover. He darts in to the attack again, his feet a blur as they shoot out at your head and body.

If you wish to try the same tactic again, turn to **422**. If you try to grapple him, turn to **142**. If you want to fall back before his attack, turn to **381**.

173

The new way you have taken plunges you deep into a dark emerald gloom, where the moisture of rotting bark seems to deaden all sound. You feel as if you are walking away from the lands of men into another time, a time of desolation and loneliness.

As you walk you begin to feel an unpleasant itching which turns to pain and, looking down, you see a horde of brown ants swarming up your legs.

There are thousands of them converging on you out of fallen trees and cracks in the earth. You run for it, brushing frantically at your body to dislodge the insects as you go.

You can head uphill (turn to **164**) or downhill (turn to **199**).

174

The magic bindings of the Tower of Will spell leave your mind and cross to the mind of the King of the Elves. You reach out and touch an alien mind, an old green-blooded mind that is at home here in the forest and unable to comprehend much of your thoughts.

Unfortunately it is as hard for you to get a grip on the king's thoughts. His will, tempered by leadership over the millennia, is at least the match of yours, and your mind, not yet fatigued by spellcasting, retreats in confusion. In a desperate flurry of thought you cast the Shield of Defence spell to protect yourself from his magic. Turn to **52**.

175

You cut a length of creeper from a nearby tree to bind the elf, who does not try to stop you tying him to a branch. 'At least now you can stop looking at me, mortal.'

As your gaze is obviously making the poor elf feel very uncomfortable you decide to spend a little time checking the area for any of his friends. You find none, though at any moment you expect to feel an arrow piercing your flesh.

When you return to the branch to check on the elf he has vanished. So has the creeper with which you tied him. All that remains is a spattering of ash on the forest floor. In the short time you were away he couldn't have got far so you search for him, but his woodcraft is superior to yours and you cannot find him. Turn to **380**.

176

Apart from the hunter and the guide there are five other people in the room. Three sit together – they look like ordinary townsfolk, suspicious but not dangerous.

Of the two others, one is a woman dressed in a grey travelling robe. The cowl is thrown back to reveal grey hair and a weather-beaten face. The remaining person is a sinister-looking man in a black cloak whose face is hidden in the shadows of his cowl.

You can sit at the nearest table to the fire and talk to hunter and guide (turn to **297**), join the woman dressed in grey (turn to **181**), or have dealings with the sinister man in black (turn to **324**).

177

You choose a suitable tree. As you prepare to slash into its bark, you glance upwards at its branches. The knots on the bole remind you of the face of a wizened old man, or perhaps of the eyes of an owl.

When you cut the bark a great flake comes off with your blade, and the pale wood beneath seems to shrink from the dim light like the stomach of an old man coughing. There is a far-away call that sounds like a howl of rage and terror lost in the wind.

The bole of the tree convulses suddenly and there is a ripping sound as its roots grow suddenly out of the ground, pinioning you.

If you have the maple flute, turn to **222**. Otherwise there is nothing you can do to save yourself as the tree, creaking and juddering, begins to sink into the ground, burying you along with it.

178

The dragon's nostrils smoulder as it looks down its long nose at you.

'You are brave, O impudent man,' it booms. Its voice has the timbre of thunder in a summer storm.

'Aye, when I have to be,' you reply, recoiling at the beast's terrifying voice. All thoughts of brave action and heroism desert you.

'What is it you want with me? Do you hanker to call yourself dragon-slayer and have your name bruited about the land? Have you perhaps heard that dragons sleep on vast hoards of treasure? Or perhaps you want me to teach you magic?'

If you say you wish to be taught the wonders of magic, turn to **185**. If you say that you would like a tenth part of the dragon's hoard, turn to **194**. If you say you want the dragon's help, turn to **205**. If you say you don't want anything from the dragon, turn to **10**.

179

As you start to pull the emerald ring off your finger you notice the owl perched on top of the ladder, looking on with its unblinking eyes.

You can take off the ring and throw it into the pool (turn to **195**), take off the ring and keep it (turn to **208**), or change your mind and leave the ring on (turn to **220**).

180

Your words seem to make no difference: the elves just stare at you. Their childlike faces belie the threat they present. A few of them carry slender longbows but these are slung over their shoulders. The elves are not trying to frighten you but the eeriness of those young old faces, silent and quizzical, is unnerving. For all you know each one of them was born before man came into existence.

You repeat that you are no friend of the Westermen and that you want to save the forest. Your words are met by a stony silence. Rattled by this lack of communication, you end up by saying that not all men are evil. You then decide to keep your mouth shut.

'I have met many men,' says a voice. 'Seven this very millennium have found me here in the greenwood. On the whole, taken for what they were, summing the sinews of their spirit and the canopy of their souls, they were bad; not evil, just bad. We came here to avoid the prattling of men. It is hard for us to be near those we must pity.'

At the mention of the word pity, many of the elves turn their faces away for a moment, as if to spare you. You will have to win their respect.

Will you apologize for making them feel uncomfortable by disturbing them in the greenwood (turn to **209**)? Or will you tell them it is they who are to be pitied, for the Westermen are destroying their forest as surely as night follows day (turn to **219**)?

181

The woman looks wise. 'My name is Elanor, I am a priestess of the All Mother, from whom springs all life, eternally.' Her weather-beaten face comes to life as she speaks and you sense her love of life.

She tells you Valerian, the man in the black robe, is a Moon Druid who vies with her for control of the forest and the beasts dwelling there. 'But they sense his evil and flock to me. His envy of me consumes his heart and turns it as black as his cloak. Valerian has thrown in his lot with the Westermen, the hewers and burners. They have come to destroy the great forest.'

She seems very grave. Will you say that it would be a terrible thing to destroy the great forest? Turn to **14**. Or will you ask her why it would be such a bad thing to destroy the forest? Turn to **2**.

182

You cast the spell of the Shield of Defence just as a silver noose appears in the air before you. The noose drops over your head magically, avoiding the shield by dancing above it. You try to drag it from your neck but the silver cord tightens slowly until it flattens your windpipe. You grow purple with effort and lack of oxygen. Gurgling horribly, unable to speak, you subside to the floor and black out, never to regain consciousness. It is doubtful that these unfriendly people of Burg will even give you a decent burial: your remains will probably be thrown on a spoil heap.

183

As Gathkeri circles you, you try to cut him off by making a sudden rush to back him up against the edge of the circle. You lunge to grapple him, but he is too quick for you this time. He skips nimbly past and falls back onto a patch of uneven ground inside the circle. He looks down when he treads on a root and you close in again.

You can repeat the same tactic (turn to **142**), attack him with your fists and feet (turn to **172**), or wait for him to attack you (turn to **161**).

184

As soon as you take the stopper out of the round bottle the bees veer away. You smear a little of the white jelly across your forehead and smile. The jelly has a pungent smell which seems to be driving the insects away. Even the beetles on the forest floor are scurrying away from you.

Saved from the insects by the white balm, you ponder where to search for the Tree of Knowledge next. You know it will soon be Midsummer's Day.

You can continue your search by heading west (turn to **43**), east (turn to **427**), or south-west (turn to **70**).

185

The dragon tells you that because you have disturbed it from its slumbers it seems appropriate to begin by teaching you the spell of sleep. It starts to recite the words of the spell, but chooses to demonstrate on you to show what the effect is like. Unfortunately it is a dragon sleep-spell and will keep a puny mortal like you asleep for a hundred years. By the time you awake the forest will be no more. Your selfish thirst for knowledge has sealed the destruction of the forest and all the things that live in it.

186

You summon all your willpower and try to grapple with the machine in a battle of minds, your resolve weakened by the nagging fear that the machine doesn't have a will of its own.

To your surprise your magic tells you there is a mind within the machine – one that belongs to the man who is controlling it. He is too busy working the machine to notice your attack, and when your psychic assault hits him the machine grinds to a halt.

You sense his shift in attention from the machine to you. Although you hold the machine motionless for many moments, you fail to overpower the will of the man inside it, and at last he manages to throw the lever that sets the steam-hammer of a sword arm into motion again.

One last great blow splits the trunk in the middle and the Tree of Life is dead. Your hopes of saving the forest are destroyed; dejected you are taken prisoner and enslaved.

187

The Elf King crosses to a juniper bush and shakes its branches. 'Attend my words,' he says to the bush. 'Awaken – speak. Tell me of a secret.'

The bush speaks in a voice like sighing: 'Under my roots, a mole with a scarred forepaw has just devoured an earthworm. No other knew this secret until now.'

The Elf Kings turns to you triumphantly. 'Well, mortal? Can you make the very plants themselves speak? If not, you forfeit the contest.'

You go over to a tree and snap off a twig. 'I shall make this single twig tell a secret,' you declare. 'And moreover, it will not be by magic, but in a manner that any man might use.' So saying, you strike up a small fire among some dead leaves and char the end of the twig. Then, removing your shirt, you use the charred tip of the twig like a pencil. The elves gather round to watch as you write: 'The Elf King's true name is—'

'Enough!' The Elf King snatches the twig out of your hand. He casts it aside, an unsettled look clouding his silver-grey eyes. 'This is mere trickery. My next task will not be so easy to circumvent.'

If you insist that it is your turn to set him a task, turn to **221**. If you let him set a third task, turn to **20**.

188

These people look very wary of strangers. Whatever you say mustn't alarm them. They could easily be untrustworthy so you had better not mention the Tree of Knowledge. You loudly announce that you are searching for a rare kind of bird that you hope to find in the forest, the violet tanager. 'Can anyone guide me to the nest of such a bird?' you ask, fingering your money-pouch significantly.

'I know of no such bird in the forest. Indeed, I have never heard tell of a tanager that was violet.' The voice of the woman in grey carries absolute certainty; she must be steeped in wilderness lore.

You explain it is a very rare bird mentioned in ancient manuscripts and ask about the birds she has seen in the forest.

She gestures you to join her table; she seems

happy to talk to you all night about the forest. The
man in the black cowl stares at you all the while; his
eyes look like glittering flints within his cowl. The
other two have returned to the fire.

Turn to **181**.

189

When you awake the Kwerrel is nowhere to be seen,
although the archway back out to the forest has
reappeared. You make good your escape, knowing
that the Kwerrel could have killed you if it had
wanted to. Turn to **406**.

190

'No,' you say loudly. 'The contest is over. I have won.'

Huldranas was already in the act of notching another arrow to his bow. He assumed that you, like any elf, would immediately accede to the king's commands. Now he lowers the bow and looks around uncertainly.

'Do you value pride above truth?' you demand of the assembled elves. 'Is this what has become of the legendary elves – cloistered from the sight of other peoples, you turn your vision inwards and forget the values of honour, courtesy and courage?'

Hundreds of faces stare back inscrutably from the gloom between the trees. The Elf King sweeps back his cloak in an extravagant gesture which reminds you of a sleek cat grooming itself. 'Very well, mortal,' he says in a languid voice. 'You have won the contest. Now let us talk.'

Turn to **232**.

191

You whip an arrow to your bow and let fly. It splinters your opponent's shaft in mid air before it reaches its target. You breathe a sigh, knowing that it was a one in a hundred fluke that you did not miss your target and end up humiliated.

The effect on Huldranas is deeply mysterious and utterly elfin. For a long moment he remains gazing along the arrow's flight, his bow half lowered, arm still poised in the moment of release. Then it is as if he wakes from a trance. Turning to you, he performs an elegant courtly salute, then snaps his bow across his knee and casts it aside along with his quiver. 'Henceforth I eschew the bow,' he declares to the assembled elves. 'Huldranas will take his prey with spear or not at all. This is my geas.'

He turns and stalks away. You regret the loss to archery of such a fine exponent of the art, but at least your daring risk has secured you victory. Now the elves will respect your words.

Turn to **232**.

192

The chance is gone. You had the opportunity not only to reach the vulnerable hose but also to jump away from your attackers. They close in from both sides and though you evade two sword cuts, a sudden thrust from behind finishes you off.

Your allies, the elves, are already melting back into the forest. You have lost your chance to save the great Forest of Arden.

193

You beg the owl's pardon and implore it to wait, but it has taken to the wing again and is swiftly lost in the gloom of the forest. As you walk away from the crags three small tree warblers dive-bomb you, pecking near your ears. They are too small to be of any danger, although you have never seen small birds act in this way. Turn to **173**.

194

The dragon flicks its tail and licks its lips. 'Walk into the cavern and behold my hoard. It has been garnered from the palaces of the whole world. Many of my pieces are old, so very old, that they have a tale to tell.'

The dragon rolls over so you fall to the ground on your feet. With a sweep of its massive claw, it ushers you forward into the dark cavern.

'All the gold and jewels you can carry I give to you.'

As you stare in awe at a pile of coins, goblets, candelabra and jewellery, some of the coins fly up into the air and push themselves against you. Soon they are covering you in a crust, like barnacles on the hull of a ship. They leave your arms and legs free but you are terribly weighed down by the gold that has stuck to you. You try to prise the coins away but they are stuck fast by the magic of the dragon.

Turn to **19**.

195

The ring slips easily off your finger, but as you take it off you feel a sense of loss – a loss of purpose and of strength. But the certainty that the ring is magical and has been influencing you strengthens your resolve. You send it spinning through the air to land in the pool with a plop.

The owl shuts its eyes and says, 'What a waste. And that was my lady's ring, not for you to hurl away.'

Delete the emerald ring from the list of possessions on your Adventure Sheet. There is still no sign of Elanor.

If you wish to steal the potions and leave, turn to **235**. If you want to ask the owl where Elanor is, turn to **244**.

196

The path twists and turns, winding through dense undergrowth overhung by barrel-like Gwelph trees that are festooned with lianas. You try to fix the shape of each tree in your mind so you will know if you have passed by one before.

To your dismay the path ends in a little clearing choked with dead leaves, but from which two paths lead off in different directions. Each path is lined with thorn bushes that have grown to the height of a man and which are covered in inch-long purple barbs oozing an orange fluid. The thorns would break off in your flesh if you brushed against them.

You can head left (turn to **131**) or right (turn to **211**). If you despair of ever finding your way out of the forest, turn to **156**. If you wish to mark one of the great Gwelph trees by scoring it with your dagger, turn to **177**.

197

The bees fly faster than you can run. They settle around your head so you cannot see to run. Blindly, you stagger about the forest, continually stung by the bees. Death from so many bee stings is not pleasant. Your neck swells until your windpipe is closed up and you choke to death. You rue bitterly your folly in upsetting Elanor, the Lady of the Forest, and you have paid the price.

198

Your heartfelt plea for the Chief of the Westermen to reconsider his actions falls upon deaf ears. He simply cannot believe you are being so foolish to question him. 'How can cutting down trees destroy the whole world? You are talking nonsense! Who are you, and who sent you to interfere in our plans?'

'Listen to me or we are all doomed,' you tell him. But now you see that you can never hope to persuade him. You have simply put yourself in danger by attempting to end the Westermen's onslaught peaceably.

The chief has had enough. 'Silence this wittering fool. Bring chains – we'll add another slave to the work gangs.'

Valerian is watching you. His hard stare suggests he is calling a spell to mind. You can surrender and be enslaved (turn to **146**), make a run for it (turn to **451**), or use magic if you have both SPELLS and a wand (turn to **450**).

199

The ants' bites are poisonous. You have already suffered dozens of wounds by the time you reach a large pond in a dark hollow. Lose 2 Life Points. Throwing caution to the winds and driven by the tormenting pain of the bites, you plunge into the water and immerse yourself where you tear off your clothes.

The torment ceases as the ants drown and float to the surface, and although the venom makes you feel drowsy you manage to drag yourself towards the pond's edge.

Just as you are about to haul yourself out of the water, you feel a huge water snake coiling around your legs.

If you want to fight the serpent, turn to **218**. If you cry out in despair to the owl in case it is still nearby and prepared to forgive and help you, turn to **227**.

200

Renard leads you out of the town through the waterside gate to the bank of the Burgstream. You walk north along a path next to the bank. The river valley has quite steep sides, making it difficult for you to see very much of the surrounding land. Ahead, however, you can see the vast top of a leafy canopy that stretches to the far horizon like a green sea fading to blue in the distance. The air is good here – fresh and clean, laden only with the perfumes of wild flowers.

A lone figure in grey walks ahead. You suggest trying to catch up but Renard just shakes his head.

'We will never find her in the forest unless she wishes it. A man might as well try to fly.'

'If we run we can catch up before she reaches the

forest,' you suggest.

'She moves as fast as a deer at need. We'd only tire ourselves to no end.'

If it is the same old woman from the inn last night, she looked too old even to break into a trot. You ponder Renard's strange claims until you can see the trunks of the trees at the edge of the Forest of Arden.

As you enter the forest you are surprised by how much colour there is. Blossoming trees, fungus mounds in bright hues, flowering creepers and giant butterflies are lit by the dappled sunshine that pours through gaps in the leafy canopy. It is noisy too – the forest is alive with insects, birds and small mammals. Renard leads you along short cuts where the Burgstream bends tortuously until at last you hear the roar of the great Sirion river as it rushes through the forest ahead. He brings you to a ford over the Burgstream.

'We must cross here and then walk west beside the Sirion.' You follow across the ford and on through the thick forest.

Nothing in your life has prepared you for the moment when you first catch sight of the Sirion river. The furthest bank is just a line of shimmering heat-hazed greenery at least six miles away. The roiling waters carry a multitude of dead tree branches towards the sea, like a vein carrying detritus out of a living body. Across the river the treeline is unbroken. You are deep in the rainforest now. The gigantic trees spread their branches more than a hundred feet above the ground. At the river's edge mangroves reach far out into the water. Bloated river buffalo bask beneath their arching roots.

'The going will be difficult for a while until we reach higher ground,' says Renard. He presses on, hacking at the undergrowth, until you reach a tributary of the river. It blocks your progress, and is spanned by only a narrow rope bridge. The bridge shows signs of regular repair: bushes have been hacked back from the stanchions between which it hangs. Renard tells you that the elves maintain this bridge as a link between different parts of their domain. He leads the way across and you follow.

He is halfway across when a waterspout surges up from the river. Out of it rears a mass of vegetation ringed with fibrous tentacles. It is a dreaded Embracer, and in seconds it has plucked Renard from the bridge. As he is pulled under the water, he manages to cry out to you: 'You must go on, then climb. Then you may find what you seek—'

The tentacles drag him under. You watch the muddied water swirl beneath the bridge, but there is no sign of poor Renard.

You can try to save him (turn to **316**) or cross the bridge quickly while the Embracer is otherwise occupied (turn to **343**).

201

The Elf King gives the order to begin. Gathkeri circles you warily. He is very light-footed and the look in his eyes is murderous.

If you want to grapple him, turn to **183**. To attack him with your fists and feet, turn to **172**. Or will you wait for him to attack you? Turn to **161**.

202

These men look well armed and well fed. They are probably veterans of many campaigns but their jowls and their paunches have grown a little flabby from lack of exercise here in the forest. The chief hired them to protect the camp against the elves, but so far the fey sylvan elves have done nothing to hinder the Westermen and the guards have led an indolent life with nothing more to do than keep the slaves in check. Still, there are eight of them and all are armed with swords and protected by corslets of mail.

If you have SWORDPLAY and a sword, you can turn to **461**. If you have CHARMS and an amulet, you can turn to **471**. If you have STREETWISE you can turn to **481**. If you have SPELLS and a wand you can turn to **442**. If you have none of these skills, turn to **491**.

203

You rush to the attack, and several of the Westermen turn to meet your onslaught. As individuals and taken one at a time they would certainly be no match for you. The men you are facing, however, are seasoned campaigners and no fools. You are quickly surrounded.

You can try to kill one, leap over his fallen body and then retreat to safer ground nearby (turn to **376**) or try to fight it out until you or all your opponents are slain (turn to **84**).

204

'Yes, that was it,' you reply. 'The Reaver's Inn, Bessaraban. What a place, eh?'

'Remember the one-legged serving wench who used to take her leg off and poke the fire with it?' asks the chief.

If you say yes, you remember her, but can't think of her name, turn to **358**. If you admit that you don't remember her, turn to **367**.

205

You explain your quest to save the forest from the Westermen. The dragon has been asleep all the time the men have been hacking and burning the forest, but he seems to believe your tales of woe. He tells you his name is Garoshtar and says he is surprised and impressed that a human could want so little of him when he has great power and riches to give.

He tells you to come for him at your hour of greatest need and he will help you against the Westermen. Remember you have the promise of Garoshtar's help. Write the codeword *Scorpion* on your character sheet.

If you have the codeword *Waterbearer* on your character sheet, turn to **49**. Otherwise, turn to **21**.

206

As he sees you about to cast another spell, Valerian utters a single word, 'Sanctuary,' in a ringing voice and claps his hands together. There is a second clap and he is gone. He has disappeared completely. You go to the door of the inn but there is no sign of him in the rain-lashed cobbled street.

Only the old woman in grey remains in the common room. If you wish to sit at her table and talk with her, turn to **181**.

If you wish only to take a room at the inn for the night, turn to **333**.

207

You summon all your willpower and try to grapple with the machine in a battle of minds, even though your resolve is weakened by the nagging fear that the machine doesn't have a will of its own.

To your surprise your magic tells you there is a mind within the machine – it belongs to the man who is controlling it. He is busy working the machine, and the machine grinds to a halt as he is hit by your psychic assault.

The operator switches his attention to you and focuses his mental powers. You hold the machine motionless for long moments without managing to overpower the will of the man inside it.

How will you follow up your success?

If you cast Choking Fog, turn to **395**. If you choose to use Bafflement, turn to **372**. If you cast Visceral Disruption, turn to **64**.

208

What if, you reason, the emerald ring is taking over control of your mind with every passing moment? As the ring slips easily off your finger you feel a sense of loss – loss of purpose and of strength. The ring must be magical. You decide to keep it safe but not to wear it for now. You need your wits about you.

The owl has been watching you all the time.

Turn to **244**.

209

'It is a mistake soon remedied by returning to the lands of men.'

'But, but . . .' you stammer as the elves turn away and slip out of sight. As they go, you look from one to another, and as you do so, each one freezes under your gaze. Perhaps they act so strangely because they are too polite to disappear while you look at them, for at the edges of your vision you see them move behind trees and leaf curtains. They vanish swiftly and silently, moving through the dense forest like rainbow trout in a murky river. They are not wasting magic, you just cannot keep up with them.

At last only one elf is left. Turn to **230**.

After leaving Burg by the waterside gate you walk north along a path next to the bank of the Burgstream. The river valley has quite steep sides and you can see little of the land that surrounds you. Ahead you see the vast leafy canopy that stretches to the far horizon like a green sea fading to blue in the distance. The air is good here, fresh and clean, laden only with the perfume of wild flowers.

A lone figure in grey walks ahead. You increase your pace to catch up. After half an hour's hard walking you seem to be no nearer the figure. You break into a jog but even this seems to bring you no closer to the slender woman dressed in grey. You ponder the strange fact that even though she seems only to be walking you cannot seem to come any closer to her. At last you reach the crest of a rise to find she has vanished, but now you can see the trunks of the trees at the edge of the Forest of Arden.

As you enter the forest you are surprised by how much colour there is. Blossoming trees, fungus mounds in bright hues, flowering creepers and giant butterflies are lit up by the dappled sunshine that trickles through gaps in the leafy canopy. It is noisy, too – the forest is alive with insects, birds and small mammals.

The path stays close to the river, almost doubling back on itself where the Burgstream bends tortuously until at last you hear the roar of the great Sirion river as it washes through the forest ahead. Pressing on, you come to a ford over the Burgstream.

If you wish to cross the ford and follow the bank of the Sirion river to the west, turn to **77**. If you prefer to remain on this side of the Burgstream and turn east when you meet the Sirion, turn to **96**.

211

The path twists and turns, winding through dense undergrowth overhung by barrel-like Gwelph trees that are festooned with lianas. You try to fix the shape of each tree in your mind so you will know if

you have passed one before. To your dismay the path ends in a little clearing choked with dead leaves. Two paths lead off in different directions, and each is lined with thorn bushes that are at least the height of a man and which are covered in inch-long purple barbs that ooze an orange fluid. The thorns would break off in your flesh if you brushed against them.

You can go left (turn to **196**) or right (turn to **131**). If you despair of ever finding your way out of the forest, turn to **156**. If you wish to orient yourself by marking one of the great Gwelph trees by scoring it with your dagger, turn to **177**.

212

There is something very strange about the grass on that hillock. It seems almost reflective, as if the stems of grass were coated in shiny wax. White egrets like the one on the hillock eat insects – they catch mites and parasites on the hides of large animals. You've never known one probe the ground for worms.

If you walk to the top of the hillock, anyway, to see what you can see, turn to **47**. If you prefer to leave the valley and skirt around it to the east, turn to **408**.

213

You tackle her before she can leap through the hatch and, pinioning her arms behind her back, tie her to a vine that is growing in and out of the walls of the tree house.

'What do you hope to gain by this?' she asks.

'The potions, what do they do?' you ask urgently.

There are five potions on the shelf behind her. There is a clear cherry red liquid in a wax-stoppered phial, a small round bottle of something like runny tar, a jar of white jelly, a cloudy sea-blue fluid in a phial and a glass pot that contains layers of coloured earth.

Elanor starts to explain what each one does. 'The blue fluid, if quaffed in sunlight, will heal all save the most serious of hurts.' As she says the word 'hurts', the back of your wrist is stung by a bee. Elanor seems not to notice and goes on talking about the potions.

'This black tarry goo is mulch of fire lizard's gizzard, a deadly poison.'

You are stung twice more, on the leg and the neck. More bees fly into the tree-house, buzzing angrily. You can't stand being stung like this for much longer. The bees' stings feel like those of hornets.

Will you quickly ask about the red liquid (turn to **313**), the white jelly (turn to **304**), or the bands of coloured earth (turn to **296**) in the hope that one of them will protect against the insects? Or will you grab the phial of blue fluid and drink it (turn to **292**)?

214

'These golden disks look pretty,' says the Kwerrel. 'Give me ten and I will help you.'

If you have 10 pieces of gold and wish to hand them over, turn to **8**. If you do not have enough or won't pay that much, turn back to **158** and choose again.

215

You recall a snippet of doggerel that used to be sung by the old gipsy women who came to town selling their handicrafts:

The name of the elfin king
Is a terribly powerful thing;
If you speak it to him, or even sing,
You can make him give you his signet ring.
The Elf King's name is—
Ah! but that would be telling!

Such songs always fascinated you, since their simple folk rhythm seems to conceal a core of hoary secret truth. The hard part is to strip away the mystery so that you are left with that truth. You also know that you must tread carefully. The elves are proud and pitiless, and often behave like spiteful children in spite of their immemorial wisdom. You must not show weakness or hesitation which they could exploit to their advantage, but neither must you offend them.

If you want to guess the Elf King's name, turn to **309**. If you would prefer to accept a duel, turn to **137**.

216

You cast a Thunderclap spell in an effort to stun the owl. The spell works and the owl, stunned, dashes its head against the branch of a tree and falls to the ground.

It lies still for a while, then raises its head to look at you.

'The curse of the Grey Touch be upon you, traveller, for striking the Grey Lady's servant,' it calls.

The owl flaps its wings and takes off, swooping past you back to the forest.

Turn to **193**.

217

You wait, concealed in the trees, for nightfall. You have not been waiting and watching long when Valerian the Moon Druid, who you saw at the inn at Burg, pays a visit to the black and scarlet pavilion. He is still wearing the all-enveloping black robe but the hood is back to reveal the hatchet-like features and black goatee beard.

He leaves an hour later, looking smugly satisfied. Other men come and go with reports or to suit for some privilege or to settle disputes.

The day fades into a dark and moonless night, ideal for what you have in mind.

If you have SPELLS and a wand and want to use magic to enter the pavilion, turn to **452**. Or you can rely on natural stealth: turn to **462**.

218

The serpent is heavy and horribly powerful. You are in its element and are powerless to resist as it crushes the life out of you. The last thing you hear is the sound of your own ribcage shattering. The forest is doomed.

219

There is no mistaking the expression in the elves' eyes this time. You have angered them.

'We are older than the forest. We were alive before the forest grew and we will live on after it is gone.'

'But it has been your home for so long. Does it not anger you to see the burners destroying its beauty?' you ask. 'And where will you live? Where will you find a place where there are no men to be pitied?'

'Have you come here to taunt us? It is the coming of the time of men. All things must pass and we with them.'

If you taunt them to goad them into action, turn to **426**. If you humble yourself and beg them to let you see the wonders of their homes in the greenwood before it is lost for ever, turn to **436**.

220

What if, with every passing moment, the emerald ring is taking control of your mind?

A long time alone in the forest, with only the noises of wild beasts for company, has made you feel vulnerable. Strange thoughts enter your head, that you are being watched, or hunted, or that you are the butt of some cruel joke for the amusement of others. Knowing that Elanor could even now be watching you is unsettling. Does she want you as her slave? Are all the birds and beasts that flock to her bidding just slaves to her whim? You know in your heart such misgivings are mere foolishness, so you decide to ignore the worry and trust in Elanor.

'Good,' says the owl, 'perhaps you really are the one to save us.'

Turn to **35**.

221

You go to stand in front of the Elf King. Then, smiling, you stand on one foot and spin around in a complete circle. You end with a bow, like a dancer acknowledging applause. 'That's the task,' you say. 'Just do as I did: turn around.'

He stares at you, violent emotion surging behind his eyes. For a long moment the two of you stand face to face, unmoving. The Elf King twitches at the hem of his cloak, grinding his feet into the sward of the forest clearing. 'Curse you!' he says at last. 'Avert your gaze and I'd do it in an instant!'

'It wouldn't count if I didn't see it,' you reply. 'Do you accept that you can't do the task?'

His regal tones are laced with sullen annoyance as he says, 'Yes, you have won the contest, mortal. I'll agree to be your ally.'

Turn to **232**.

222

You take out the flute and set it to your lips. The tree, creaking and shuddering, begins to sink into the ground, taking you down with it. Drawing a large breath you blow as hard as you can and an eerie half-heard note seems to sound far away. Then the forest seems to go quiet as the background noise of chattering, piping and warbling gives way to eerie silence. The tree roots fall away from you and are drawn slowly back into the ground.

A little tree frog, lime green with scarlet spots, jumps onto your shoulder and then down on to the ground. It begins to hop away and, not knowing what else to do, you follow. Soon it has led you to a previously unnoticed path that winds between the thorn bushes. Without the flute you would have been lost in the forest for ever.

Turn to **237**.

223

Your feint works. This time it is the elf who is overcommitted and you who can strike without fear. Your sword crashes into his side and the elf doubles up and falls to the floor. He cries his submission. One of his kind rushes forward with a healing potion to stem the tide of green blood, which coats his clothes like pond slime.

You have won the duel. Turn to **263**.

224

Renard's cottage is small but well looked after. He lives alone and is a tactiturn fellow. He asks for one piece of gold for every day he is with you, and before he even agrees to guide you he wants to see the colour of your money. You show him your gold, but are mindful to sleep with the money pouch under your mattress.

In the morning Renard is up early and he brings

you some steaming broth to eat before you set out. He says he will need another piece of gold for every day it takes to travel back to Burg from wherever you part company.

If you agree to his terms, turn to **200**. If you would rather risk the forest alone, turn to **210**.

225

'What care I for those who dwell in the forest?' The little imp starts to sing in a high wistful tone, 'I works and sings from dusk till dawn, no lark more blithe than me, and this the burden of my song forever doomed to be – I care for nobody. No, not I, and nobody cares for me.'

Will you tell the Kwerrel how sad you are that he must be lonely (turn to **323**). Or that he will be cared for if he helps to save the forest (turn to **284**)?

226

Once again the elf's dirk scores your flesh. Lose 4 Life Points. If you still live, you gain heart when you notice that the elf too is tiring. You manage to wound him and corner him between two trees that grow close together.

Your opponent drops the dirk and says he will take you to the King of the Elves in Elvenhame.

If you have a potion of red liquid and wish to drink it, it will magically heal all your lost Life Points. If you wish to keep the elven dirk note it on your Adventure Sheet. Turn to **331**.

227

As if materializing at your call the owl swoops and claws at the serpent's eyes. The snake falls back under the water and you scramble out of the mud and catch your breath under the trees, watching the surface of the pond warily.

'So now you know. It pays to have friends in the forest,' says the bird. 'Follow me.' It flits away through the trees and then waits for you to come near before flying onward.

Turn to **241**.

228

Garoshtar sights one of the columns of men that are blundering their way through the forest, flattening trees and bushes as they go. There are thousands of soldiers, most of them sweating inside chain armour. Near the front is a contingent of three hundred crossbowmen, all dressed in the same mail and uniform, obviously mercenaries. There is no sign of any infernal machines with this column.

You can ask Garoshtar to search out the second column the elven scouts saw advancing upon the Tree of Life (turn to **248**), or to attack these men while they are vulnerable in a clearing (turn to **273**).

229

You bide your time until you are roughly unhooked from the coffle chain and set to work digging a hole for the Westermen to use as a latrine. When the guard looks away you cast a Vanish spell and make good your escape. The guard has just returned to the pit you had begun to dig and is looking around for you. If he doesn't want to call attention to the fact he has let you escape he may do nothing. On the other hand he may sound the alarm.

Will you try to free the innkeeper, which you must surely do if you promised his daughter you would try to find him (turn to **264**). Or will you abandon him to the Westermen's tender mercies (turn to **279**)?

230

'Why have all your friends gone? Why won't they talk to me?'

'They are elves, they do not wish to.'

'You are an elf, you are still here talking to me.'

'But I do not wish to.'

'Then why do you not vanish like the rest?'

'Shut your eyes just for a moment.'

Will you do as the elf asks (turn to **240**)? Or keep your gaze firmly on the last of the slippery elves (turn to **250**)?

231

Judging from your manners and bearing, the guard has no reason to doubt you, and deferentially leads you to the pavilion. You step inside and introduce yourself to an important-looking man – the Chief of the Westermen – sitting at a large oak table strewn with scrolls and maps. A balding corpulent man, his eyes seem to gleam with greed.

His eyes show a vague flicker of recognition, and
you hope wits will see you through this meeting. For
now, however, there seems to be little to worry
about. The chief invites you to look at the master
map which shows the whole Forest of Arden. A
broad swathe of brown has recently been painted
across the green of the forest and a red point marks
each of the Westermen encampments which are
eating into the forest. The chief waves his broad
hand across the map, showing where they are going
to wreak devastation and havoc next. Right in the
centre of the triangle made by the Bonehill, the
bower of the Lady of the Forest and the geysers, a
small pool with an ancient-looking Greenbark tree
drawn on it has been carefully painted in.

You can ask him about the Tree of Knowledge (turn to **337**), why the chief is despoiling the forest (turn to **97**), or if there is ever any trouble among the slaves or his own men (turn to **354**).

232

The Elf King tells you there are about twelve thousand elves here in the forest, and a very few spread across the rest of the world who are too far away to be reached in time.

Write the codeword *Waterbearer* on your Adventure Sheet.

If you have the codeword *Bullhorn* on your Adventure Sheet, turn to **256**. Otherwise, turn to **42**.

233

The stone misses the owl, which veers into the top of a tree. It clings on to a branch there and struggles upright, then while preening its ruffled feathers says, 'The curse of the Grey Touch be upon you, for striking at the servant of the Lady of Grey.' The owl swoops down past you back to the forest.

Turn to **193**.

234

Zorolotl is too quick for you. The desperate nature of your last ditch attack only makes it easier for him to sidestep you and cut into your side, below your armpit. Lose 8 Life Points.

If you are still alive, turn to **238**.

235

You carefully gather the potions. Note them on your Adventure Sheet: you have a red potion, a tarry black potion, a white jelly, a cloudy blue potion, and a jar of coloured earth.

As you climb down the ladder to the ground you discover that Elanor is nowhere to be seen, but her owl is still gazing at you unblinkingly. It follows as you leave the clearing. Just then you become aware of a loud droning sound in the air above the clearing, and there is a stab of pain as a bee stings the back of your neck. Looking back, you see a shadow pass through the beams of green-filtered sunlight as a whole swarm of bees flies to attack you.

Will you run in search of water to hide in (turn to **197**), smear some of the white jelly on yourself (turn to **184**), smear some of the black tar on yourself (turn to **168**), drink the blue potion (turn to **155**), or drink the red potion (turn to **141**)?

236

The little imp's eyes light up when he sees the emerald ring. 'It is the Lady's ring, the ring of power.' He yanks it off your finger and runs to the central trunk of the giant bush. He scrambles up just as if he were a monkey, writhing sinuously past the wicked barbed thorns. You could never follow him. He chirrups and laughs, looking down at you through the thorny branches. You ask him to keep his side of the bargain, to help you in your quest.

'I am the Kwerrel, the Kwerrel keep no bargains.'

His chirruping laugh mocks you.

Will you tell him to put on the ring (turn to **15**), or use SPELLS against him, if you have that skill as well as a wand (turn to **375**)?

237

You trudge on, singling out a particular tree to head for as far away as you can see and keeping it in sight as you go to try to make sure you don't walk in circles. When you reach the tree you look back and try to identify the one you left behind so that you can choose another tree to make for in the same general direction. It is tiring and you are exhausted.

Moving through winding mossy ways, wrapped in the green gloom of the forest depths, you catch the scent of unusual blooms. A path fringed with violet blossoms leads off between the great black boles of the trees, and following it with your gaze you glimpse a stone tower. It is some distance out of your path, and ominously draped in shadows.

If you want to investigate the tower, turn to **394**. If you pass by without looking back, turn to **454**.

238

'Submit; your red blood stains the sward. You have fought well. Honour is satisfied. Submit.' The elf shows no pity but you fancy you can see admiration for your courage in his eyes.

Will you give in and submit to Zorolotl (turn to **344**)? Or fight on in the hope of triumphing against the odds (turn to **269**)?

239

You manage to creep to within twenty paces of the silk pavilion before one of the guards sees you and raises the alarm. You run back towards the forest edge but a detachment of soldiers issues from the trees; they fan out and surround you. Fearing the worst you are relieved when they only take you prisoner. Turn to **151**.

240

You close your eyes for a moment, then pondering how hard it has been to find them and how important is your quest, you open them again to make sure the elf is not slinking away. But already you are too late. In a blink of the eye the last elf has vanished. You stomp through the undergrowth calling and searching but the only answer is the high mocking laughter of the elves as they recede into the depths of the forest. You have failed to meet the elves on Midsummer's Day.

You can try again tomorrow (turn to **139**), or abandon all hope of persuading the elves to help save their own forest (turn to **280**).

241

The owl leads you by easy ways and you make faster progress than before. It seems to be leading you many miles and before nightfall you have to ask it to stop so you can rest.

The next day you begin to wonder whether the owl is not merely leading you astray. When you ask how much further to the bower it always says the same thing: 'Not far. Follow me.' You come to hate the sight of the bird that keeps you slogging through the forest in its wake.

You are about to stop in protest that it has been saying not far all day long, when you notice in this part of the forest no two trees are the same species. It is as if every type of tree in the forest has one representative here. You comment on this to the owl, but when you look round you realize it has vanished.

Turn to **259**.

Turn to **259**.

242

As soon as you take the stopper out of the round bottle the bees fly out of the tree-house. You smear a little of the white jelly across your forehead and smile. The jelly has a pungent smell which seems to be driving the insects away. Even the beetles on the tree-house floor are scurrying away from you.

You carefully gather up all the other potions. Note all the potions on your Adventure Sheet: you have a cherry-red potion, a tarry-black potion, a white jelly, a cloudy blue potion, and a jar of many-coloured earth. Then you climb down the ladder to the ground and consider your next move.

From here you can go west (turn to **43**), east (turn to **427**), or south-west (turn to **70**).

243

'A magic potion for me, the Kwerrel? Oh yes, how fine, how very fitting. Must I quaff it now? Will I be able to speak words of power and conjure spells, and make monsters do my bidding?'

If you give the Kwerrel a blue potion, turn to **254**. If you give him the white jelly, turn to **265**. If you give him the red liquid, turn to **275**. Cross the appropriate potion off your Adventure Sheet.

244

'Come, follow,' says the owl. 'I will take you to My Lady of the Forest.'

'To Elanor?' you ask.

'Yes, follow.'

The owl leads you along a maze of paths to a dark bower ringed with hawthorns. You would never have found it without the owl to lead you. An archway has been cut through the thick haws and Elanor stands inside the bower, pouring water from a silver ewer into a jade bowl on a stone plinth. She looks as beautiful as ever, but sinister too in the shadows.

Write the codeword *Twinhead* on your Adventure Sheet. Turn to **46**.

245

Your sword skill triumphs. The elf dodges the feinted thrust but succumbs to the cut that drives your blade into his stomach; he staggers and you finish him off with a single chop across the back of the head.

Drawing breath, you listen for others, realizing that at any moment you may be picked off by the arrows of his kind. If you wish to take the elf's dirk note it on your Adventure Sheet. You hurry quickly through the dense underbrush and stumble across a very strange old monument covered in creepers and partially knocked down by a fallen pine. It must once have been a great victory arch, perhaps built here before the forest itself grew here, or to commemorate a victory against rebels who had hidden out in the trees. This is not elven architecture. It is the first sign of man since you entered the Forest of Arden.

Turn to **289**.

246

Renard is beginning to panic as he weakens from loss of blood. He curses you for a murderous fool. As you wonder how you could have been so foolish as to attack the tentacles clutching him, the Embracer erupts out of the water beneath you once more.

Turn to **287**.

247

You wait in Elvenhame until the elven scouts report on Garoshtar's success. They tell you that the great dragon has attacked the Westermen and set them back in confusion. After many attacks, however, he was wounded by many crossbow quarrels and forced to land and sleep so he could heal himself. He has won you precious time, however, and the defence of the Tree of Life is now set in hand.

Turn to **57**.

248

Garoshtar's great body puts the men in shadow for a moment as he swoops overhead and you are satisfied to see the soldiers below like helpless little ants on the forest floor.

If you have AGILITY turn to **319**. Otherwise Garoshtar swoops low, his wings cracking down at the last moment as he swings his head and breathes over the leading company of soldiers, sending a cloud of poisonous gas and acid roiling about them. His wings crack against the air as he struggles to gain height, skimming the treetops. The mercenaries let loose their crossbows as one and Garoshtar is stuck like a pincushion. The dragon convulses in mid air, throwing you off his back and you impale yourself on a branch of the tree below. The forest is doomed.

249

You cry a single word of power and vanish, to reappear an instant later with two copies of yourself to your left. You and they remain motionless, for if you move the illusion will be broken and the visions will fade.

Now you must chose another spell. There is little point in casting Vanish, so will you choose Choking Fog (turn to **143**), Visceral Disruption or Bafflement (turn to **347**), Shield of Defence (turn to **326**), or Tower of Will (turn to **91**)?

250

'Why do you stare at me so? Are you trying to turn me to stone?' asks the elf. He grins at you but you notice he is quivering tensely.

'I'm not letting you slip away,' you say, 'I have travelled far to find you and now that I have, you will not talk to me.'

'Why should I talk to a mortal? You know so little, one might as well talk to a mole or a dung beetle. You cannot hope to understand us and the way of our world.'

'In any case I'm not taking my eyes off you.'

The elf's skin seems to fade almost to pearly white as you say this. He sits crosslegged in front of you. 'Then I'll just have to wait for you to go to sleep.' He feigns nonchalance but seems very uncomfortable under your gaze. At last he says, 'Tie me up if you must, but release me from your stare or I shall go mad.'

It seems your gaze alone holds him in thrall. Fascinating. You ask him what power you have over him.

'An elf can never turn his back when looked on by mortal eyes. Your gaze entraps us as surely as if you had shackled us in cold iron. This is why we shun mankind, and rarely show ourselves. There, you have forced the secret from my lips. Will you look away and release me now?'

You can look away out of kindness (turn to **330**) or demand that the elf takes you to meet his king (turn to **340**).

251

You sit down in the clearing and cover yourself with leaves so that you can just see out. Remaining motionless for a long time you wait until the denizens of the clearing, a group of miniature deer with heads like little hippopotamuses, return to their grooming ground. By watching them for some time you notice many leave the clearing by the left path and then disappear behind the trunk of a tree. Rising from the mound of leaves you investigate and find a small path winding between the thorn bushes. Without the wit to use such tricks of the woods you would have been lost in the forest for ever.

Turn to **237**.

252

The man in black fixes you with a flinty stare. 'What are you doing here, stranger?' He awaits your reply in stony silence.

If you have STREETWISE, turn to **188**. Otherwise, will you tell him to mind his own business (turn to **336**) or that you seek the Tree of Knowledge (turn to **124**)? If you wish simply to leave the inn abruptly, turn to **117**.

253

As you draw back your sword to strike, Elanor suddenly jerks the end of a vine. A secret hatch opens in the side of the tree-house. She jumps through and swings to the ground on a hanging creeper.

'You will never leave the forest,' she warns. 'I

will turn every living thing against you.'

Inside the tree-house you are stung on the cheek by a bee. Then another stings your wrist. More bees fly in, buzzing angrily. In your haste to flee you can grab only three of the five potions. There is a clear cherry-red liquid in a stoppered phial, a small round bottle of something like runny tar, a jar of white jelly, a cloudy sea-blue fluid in a phial and a glass pot banded with layers of coloured earth. Note which three you are taking on your Adventure Sheet.

You rush to climb down the ladder to the ground. Turn to **322**.

254

Without waiting to hear a word the impish little Kwerrel puts the potion bottle to his mouth and begins to drink greedily. He is drinking the mulch of fire lizard's gizzard, as deadly a poison to him as it is to you. He dies in a fit of convulsions, leaving you alone.

There is nothing to be done for the poor little Kwerrel, so you begin to search for a way out of the giant bush. At last your perseverance is rewarded and you break out into the open – but not without getting badly scratched by the thorns. Lose 1 Life Point and turn to **406**.

255

'I submit!' you cry. 'You are the victor.'

The King of the Elves looks at you with contempt. 'Such magics as you can muster will not prevail over the Westermen. Leave the forest. You have a week to clear the edge of the forest or your life will be forfeit.' Turn to **384**.

256

Later, seated in a ring with the elven elders, you are planning your defence of the Tree of Life when a messenger runs into the clearing and bows to the king. 'The Westermen are moving, sire, in two columns. They are heading for the Tree of Life – more men than there are ants in a Gwelph tree.'

'How long will they take to reach the Tree of Life?' you ask.

'Three days, perhaps four, no more.'

'How long will it take to marshal all your elves?' you ask anxiously.

He returns a bleak time-haunted look. 'A week; it can't be done in less. The forest is so large . . .'

You must think of a way of delaying the Westermen until the elves are ready.

If you have the codeword *Scorpion* on your Adventure Sheet, turn to **11**.

If not, you can try to assassinate the chief of the Westermen (turn to **433**), journey to the Bonehill to talk with the dragon (turn to **54**), or lead as many elves as you can muster into pitched battle before the Tree of Life (turn to **30**).

257

Zorolotl seems content to let you come forward and make the next strike. He is counting on his nimbleness saving him if you commit yourself as clumsily as you did last time, then he will riposte. How much more of this can you stand?

Will you try to end it quickly with a blistering combination of attacks? Turn to **234**.

Or will you feint and draw him in, to make him commit himself? Turn to **223**.

258

'Yes, I am lost,' you reply. 'Are you truly a talking owl?'

'Truly I am. I suppose you want to know how to escape from the forest?'

You are tempted to say yes but pride will not let you. The owl sounds surprised when you say no.

'Humans usually want to know the way out. It is a hard place for those who do not know and love the forest.'

The owl seems friendly, if it really is the owl talking. It tells you it is an enchanted bird, enchanted by the Lady of Grey, to bring those who are friends of the forest to her bower.

Will you ask the owl to take you to the Lady in Grey (turn to **241**)? Or will you ask the way to find the Tree of Knowledge (turn to **328**)?

259

You walk slowly on past a blue cedar that stands beside a tall poplar tree. The trees are festooned with climbing plants and a spiral of violet wistaria climbs the poplar like a barber's pole. The forest seems to quieten around you as you push under a hanging curtain of clematis and honeysuckle and enter a small clearing which is a beautifully tended garden. An inner ring of fruit trees surrounds the meadow-like garden, which is lit with bright sun that bathes the wings of butterflies and dragonflies glittering with iridescent hues. Behind a large pool in the meadow is a gnarled old holm-oak tree with a ladder leading up to a tree-house.

The owl is perched on top of the tree-house. 'I told you it wasn't far. If only you didn't walk so slowly.'

'Enough; do not chide. We must make our visitor welcome.' A woman in a pearl-grey robe pulls aside a raffia curtain at the top of the ladder and beckons you welcomingly. She is young and very beautiful. You find her appearance startling. Who would have expected to encounter such loveliness in this remote place? Looking upon one so serene makes you think of the fabled Faerie Queen.

If you have CHARMS and an amulet, turn to **283**. Otherwise, if you have the maple flute, turn to **299**. If not, turn to **310**.

260

Climbing a rise you look out over a scene of utter devastation. The trees have been chopped down as far as the eye can see. An infernal engine of some kind belches black smoke and two hundred yards away you see a forge with a gigantic cauldron over a bonfire which six men feed constantly with ready-cut wood and charcoal. The men working here are very pale skinned, their faces long and thin, like hatchets. They shout to each other over the din of the engine in a language you don't understand.

Teams of horses yoked together pull logs to where groups of men cut them up with saws, ready for burning. A row of children sit nearby; they are darker skinned than the men and have been set to toil over sharpening the saws.

Where the trees have been felled and stripped men are torching the underbrush to kill everything that lives in the forest. A pall of smoke hangs over everything like a storm-cloud.

The men haven't noticed you yet. There is a group of armed guards near the forge who sport more steel armour than you have ever seen. These men must be wealthy. They also look bored and edgy.

Will you show yourself and talk to them, (turn to 100)? Or will you sink back into the forest and hide (turn to 134)?

261

You look away and say that you free the elf to return to his home. There is no answer: you look back in time to se the dirk being thrust at your throat. The elven blade cuts your jugular and you fall to the ground in a dying faint.

262

The sword cuts cleanly through the fibres lopping the tentacles into pieces. The Embracer emits a piercing shriek and throws Renard at you before subsiding once more into the river. You both swim to the far bank before the Embracer can recover.

Turn to **398**.

263

The eyes of the elves still hold no clue as to what they think of you. They do not clap or smile or acknowledge your victory in any way, but the king says, 'You have proved your worth in the duel. Elvendom will play its part if you lead us against the Westermen for there is not one of us who wants to see the destruction of the forest. What would you have us do?'

As he says this, you are given a clear blue potion to drink which makes your whole body tingle excruciatingly, but heals any of your hurts. Note that all your Life Points are restored.

'Come. We will plan the downfall of the Westermen,' says the Elf King.

Turn to **232**.

264

The innkeeper is chained in a line of five slaves who have been set to repair a broken cartwheel. Four of them lift the cart while another tries to tie a joint together. The guard comes over to the group and starts kicking them to give himself the feeling he is doing his job well. The innkeeper groans and begs for mercy as the guard's boot thumps into his stomach. He groans again.

Will you kill the guard (turn to **315**)? Or bide your time (turn to **334**)?

265

The Kwerrel sniffs at the pot of ointment and tastes a smear. He wrinkles his nose in disgust and throws the pot back at you. If you have AGILITY you can leap over the toadstool and catch it before it lands on the ground and breaks (restore it to your Adventure Sheet). Otherwise it shatters against a flint and is lost. You will have to offer the Kwerrel imp something else.

Turn back to **158** and choose again.

266

You cast Vanish and disappear. Then you creep slowly round to the porch of the pavilion and, waiting to make sure there will be no one coming in or out you creep in and sneak behind the table where the man they call the chief is seated, poring over maps. He is a balding, corpulent man whose eyes gleam with greed.

The master map shows the Forest of Arden in its entirety. A broad swathe of brown has recently been painted across the green of the forest and a red point marks each of the Westermen encampments which are eating into the forest. The chief waves his broad hand across the map, showing where they are going to wreak devastation and havoc next. Right in the centre of the triangle made by the Bonehill, the bower of the Lady of the Forest and the geysers, a small pool with an ancient-looking Greenbark tree drawn on it has been carefully painted in. There is nothing to show where Elvenhame, the fabled city of the elves, is.

The chief dismisses his scribes and furls the map once more before you can read any of the little notes the scribes have inked in.

Will you stay to see if you can discover more, bearing in mind your spell will fail in another ten minutes or so (turn to **115**)? Or will you leave now while the coast is clear (turn to **95**)?

267

Your charm of friendship works. The egret flies up into the air, arcs round you in a graceful curve and comes to land on your head. It has stopped its cackling. You start to climb the hillock with the white egret balancing on your head. As you set foot on the hillock you are surprised at how hard the ground feels, yet it yields slightly as if a layer of hard rock was resting on mud. The ground is smooth and has a sheen: it only looked like grass. You climb on up the hillock and reaching the summit, look down on its far side which is ribbed and ridged in the most unusual way. It dawns on you that the thing you are standing on is a gargantuan dragon. You can see its head, the size of a cart, curled up next to its feet as it slumbers. It seems not to have noticed you crawling like a fly over its great body.

Will you climb down its head and slay it (turn to **116**)? Or will you attempt to wake it up and perhaps talk with it, for they say some dragons can talk (turn to **178**)?

268

'The Elf King's name,' suggests the mirror-sprite. 'That is a very old secret.'

You shrug. 'What of it? I need a secret that will help me in my quest.'

'Among the ancient folk, names are especially significant,' says the sprite. 'You can force such a being to do what you want if you know his name. And you might want the Elf King's help before your quest is done.'

'All right, what is his name?'

The sprite demurs. 'I heard . . . on the wind, long ago, I heard a whisper . . .' It glances to left and right, wearing a fearful expression on your own reflected face. 'I'll tell you this rhyme:

'The name of the Elven King
Is a very powerful thing;
If you speak it to him, or even sing,
He'll have to give you his signet ring.'

You give the mirror a long hard glare. The sprite returns your annoyance with a disingenuous look. 'That does not sound very helpful,' you say coldly.

'It is all I dare,' replies the sprite. 'Now, hurry – shatter the mirror so that I can fly free.'

Write the codeword *Speculum* on your Adventure Sheet. Now, if you break the mirror, turn to **418**. If not, turn to **105**.

269

The Elf is angered by your refusal to give in. You try to defend yourself, but hampered as you are by your wounds you are no match for him. He thrusts fast twice, each time cutting you deeply. You are drenched in your own hot red blood as the elf stands back, looking on you sorrowfully as he can see that he has killed. Another elf rushes forward with a potion and holds it to your mouth to drink, but he is too late. A wracking cough shakes you and you die.

270

The elves take you by secret ways through the forest until you come near to the camp of the Westermen. There they leave you. If they are seen by mortal men they become unable to melt away into the forest and are then in danger of being enslaved, so you will have to spy alone. Turn to **260**.

271

Your swiping sword point just keeps the elf at bay. He is quick and nimble. But after a while you realize he is hampered because he cannot flee. He can only walk backwards, feeling his way. His eyes seem drawn to yours as you press your attack. Will you try one mighty lunge to end the fight (turn to **291**) or a combination, feinting a high thrust and following up with a chop to the midriff (turn to **245**)?

272

Seeing that you have broken the terms of the duel by failing to submit when you have been beaten, the King of the Elves feels he may use death magic against you. He frowns hard at you and begins a chant. Your blood congeals and blocks your arteries. Your heart beats frantically, trying to force the blood to your brain but the strain is too great and your heart bursts. You have been slain for breaking the rules of the duel.

273

If you have AGILITY turn to **286**. Otherwise Garosh-tar swoops low, his wings cracking down at the last moment as he swings his head down and breathes over the leading company of soldiers, sending a cloud of poisonous gas and acid roiling about them. His wings crack hard against the air as he struggles to gain height, skimming the treetops. The mercenaries let loose their crossbows as one and Garoshtar is stuck like a pincushion. The dragon convulses in mid air, throwing you off his back and you impale yourself on a branch of a tree. The forest is doomed.

274

The earth mound that was to be your bed collapses beneath you. It is the home of a giant man-eating Colossus beetle. You try to puzzle out what has happened in the pitch dark. Then as the chitinous walls of the throat of a Colossus beetle press you down its gullet you realize you have been swallowed

alive while you listened for a monster stalking you.
Nothing will avail you now as the acid of the beetle's
stomach does its work. If only you had a guide who
might have warned that the mound of earth on which
you chose to sleep was the cap of a Colossus beetle's
burrow.

275

Without waiting to hear your answer the impish little
Kwerrel puts the potion bottle to his mouth and
begins to drink greedily.

'Not yet,' you caution. 'Drink only at need when
you are hurt and need magical healing.' The Kwerrel
stops drinking and examines the joint of his thumb
carefully.

'It is working: you tell the truth, my thumb is healed.' He sucks on it happily. 'Take some of the flesh of the toadstool. It is the Blood of Iron toadstool. Make an infusion with elderflower wine and give it to any being you wish to drug into sleep. They will sleep the sleep of the damned. Look, now I open the archway for you to leave.'

You take a large piece of the flesh of the toadstool (note it among your possessions) and, bidding good-bye to the little imp, you walk back out into the forest. Turn to **406**.

276

Your arrow slices through the air and strikes exactly where Huldranas hit a moment before, splintering the shaft in two. It is a good hit. You allow yourself a self-satisfied nod and lower your bow, then turn to Huldranas. He lets fly with a second arrow, attempting to do the same to your shaft embedded in the branch, but in his haste he is careless and the shot goes wide, missing the branch entirely.

'That is sufficient,' you say. 'I've no desire to humiliate you. Admit you're bested.'

'No,' interrupts the Elf King. 'Let Huldranas try again.'

If you allow Huldranas to make a second attempt at splitting your arrow, turn to **300**. If you insist that the contest ends now that you have proven yourself the victor, turn to **190**.

277

The days come and go and still you cannot find anyone to talk to in the forest, nor anything but perfectly ordinary-seeming trees. You manage to find enough berries and nuts to stay alive but it is a hard existence. The forest is just too big to find your way through alone.

For hours on end you feel as though you are being watched by unseen eyes. Sometimes you whirl round suddenly, eyes darting towards any sign of movement, in the hope of catching one of the spies. But you never do.

Then one day which dawns cold and dewy just like any other, you hear a strange thumping and an occasional hissing like a dragon's breath or a geyser erupting far away. Turn to **260**.

278

Your spell, which should have stunned the egret and sent it to sleep for a while, goes off much more strongly than you expected. There is an explosion and a cloud of white feathers flutters to the charred earth, all that remains of the white egret. The report rolls around the valley, echoing ominously. The hillock begins to shake as if in an earthquake. The ground you have stepped back on is quite firm but you can feel the vibrations rocking you slightly. Then the whole of the green hillock rolls upwards and away from you, leaving you standing on the edge of a ledge with a twenty-foot drop. As the hillock moves it creases and splits apart and you realize what it is. It turns its great scaly neck like a corkscrew and looks back over its shoulder at you. You are looking into the face of a dragon; the smouldering red eyes gaze at you like the portals to hell out of its cart-sized face.

Will you leap at its head to attack it before it can wake up (turn to **74**)? Or smile at it and hope it doesn't eat you, while preparing a spell, if you know how (turn to **36**)?

279

You have no difficulty in making your way back into the forest unchallenged. The guard thought better of raising the alarm. He goes over to some other slaves and starts kicking them to give himself the feeling he is doing his job well. You hear the innkeeper groan and beg for mercy.

Soon the awful sights and sounds of the Westerman camp are far behind.

You can head west (turn to **43**), east (turn to **427**), south-west (turn to **70**), or south (turn to **78**).

280

You abandon the elves but continue with your quest for the Tree of Knowledge. You are still no nearer finding it when you stumble across the bodies of hundreds of elves lying among the trees. It is as if someone has just switched them off without warning, some even while eating their supper. They are all dead and the forest is doomed. You will never escape.

281

Renard snorts in disgust. 'Not that old tale again. Don't let Marek tell you it was as big as a temple, will you?' He gets up and leaves.

Marek the Hunter fixes you with a grim stare. Whatever he thinks he has seen has really frightened him.

'It was like a small green hill. I almost stepped on it. But its body heaved as it breathed. I thought it was asleep. I backed away from the clearing but it opened one eye, like a moon, and looked at me. Its nostrils smoked and I thought it was going to kill me, but it let me go and I ran all the way out of the forest by nightfall of the fourth day.'

You ask the hunter if he could find this clearing again but he seems too fearful. You ask him to draw a map but he says he cannot write. 'But if you walk beside the Burgstream to the banks of the great Sirion river, turn west and then climb where the ground rises, you will find the place.'

Marek pleads tiredness and excuses himself. You follow suit and take a room in the inn for the night. Turn to **333**.

282

'How am I to find my way back out of the forest?' asks Pozzo. 'I am a man of the town. I was lost before the Westermen dogs captured me. I'll never see Burg or my poor daughter again without your help.'

Will you change your mind and take the time

needed to escort him to Burg (turn to **62**)? Or will you tell him to walk until he finds a river and then to follow that river towards the sea and he will one day escape the forest (turn to **12**)?

283

You whisper a charm and rub the pendant on your neck chain. The magical stone is not warm – there seems to be no danger – yet there is something about the Lady in Grey that suggests power. If you have the maple flute turn to **299**. Otherwise, turn to **310**.

284

'I don't care to be cared for. We Kwerrel can look out for ourselves.' He seems angered. Perhaps he hates to be pitied.

'I will hold you prisoner here for a day, or a month or a year . . . until I have grown tired of you.' With that the imp disappears high into the giant bush, his chirruping laughter mocking you. You start to look for a way out of the giant bush of thorns. Turn to **432**.

285

The wind takes the Choking Fog and blows it into the face of the King of the Elves. He staggers, while the two images to his right remain immobile, and he clutches at his throat and begins to vomit. He calls out his submission as he falls retching to the ground.

You can cancel the spell and save him (turn to **353**) or let the spell run its course (turn to **365**).

286

Garoshtar swoops low, his wings cracking down at the last moment as he swings his head down and breathes over the leading company of soldiers, sending a cloud of poisonous gas and acid roiling about them. His wings crack hard against the air as he struggles to gain height, skimming the treetops. The mercenaries let loose their crossbows as one and Garoshtar is stuck like a pincushion. The dragon convulses in mid air, but you manage to cling on. The wounds are not mortal but Garoshtar tells you he must land and sleep for a few years to heal his many hurts. He lands near Elvenhame and sinks immediately into a deep slumber, his bulk rising and falling in time with his breathing like a heavy ocean swell. You decide to search for the Elf King to report what has befallen brave Garoshtar. Turn to **57**.

287

You grab one of the tentacles with your free hand and try to climb towards the head of the Embracer. It beats you back with its tentacles and one coils around your sword arm. The tentacles constrict around your wrist like a noose of steel and the sword falls from your grasp. Unfortunately the creature has more than enough tentacles to deal with you and soon both your arms are crushed to your sides by what feel like iron bars. The Embracer drags you down to the slimy bottom and waits for you to drown, before feeding. You will never see the Tree of Life now. The Forest of Arden is doomed.

288

You cast the dirk, not expecting it to hit the bird, but it flashes through the air and buries itself in the egret's breast. The bird croaks once and falls lifeless to the burnt floor of the valley. Cross the dirk off your list of possessions.

If you walk to the top of the hillock to see what you can see, turn to **314**. If you prefer to leave the valley and skirt around it to the east, turn to **429**.

289

As you stare at the crumbled victory arch a sense of hopelessness overwhelms you. There is very old, very bad magic here, you can feel it in your bones. You are hopelessly lost now and will never see the lands of men again. This is what all man's labours come to with the passing of time.

You are still searching for the Tree of Life when you come across the bodies of hundreds of dead elves among the trees. It is as though they have all been switched off suddenly, cut off in the midst of immortal life, some even as they ate their supper. The elves are all dead and you and the forest are doomed.

290

You wriggle and squirm but can't evade the crushing arm. The breath is driven out of your body and you are helpless as the statue crushes your chest against its own. You die and the statue attacks the Tree of Life remorselessly. When the tree is slain the elves and the forest will die with it.

291

Your lunge is mighty indeed but the point of your sword only cuts through air. The nimble elf jumps aside, rolls and, as you turn to face him once more, you feel the cold steel of his dirk biting deep into your side. Lose 5 Life Points. The elf pulls the dirk out and begins to circle you.

You can fight on (turn to **226**) or let the elf go by looking away (turn to **261**).

292

You grab the phial and down the cloudy blue fluid. Elanor makes no move to stop you. 'I have tricked you, fool. You have just drunk the mulch of the fire lizard's gizzard. You have not long to live.'

Elanor is right. Your throat goes into spasm as the poison starts to work and soon you cannot breathe. You can do nothing as Elanor pulls on a vine and a secret hatch opens in the side of the tree-house. She pushes you through it and you fall to the ground, finding merciful release from the pain and the poison. The ants will dine on you tonight.

293

The mesmerizing look in Zorolotl's eyes is gone: they are dimmed with pain. He has lost so much blood he can hardly see straight. Realizing he cannot fight on, Zorolotl submits to you, saying you are the victor in the duel. A young elf runs up with potions for both of you to drink which he assures you will restore you to complete health. Turn to **263**.

294

The wind takes the Choking Fog and blows it back in your direction.

Will you step right back to avoid it so that it obscures you from your foe (turn to **306**)? Or stand your ground and cancel the spell (turn to **318**)?

295

You charge the Infernal Statue and rain blows down upon it, but the metal is not dented by the mightiest of your blows. In hammering against the statue with all your might you break your sword off at the hilt. You will have to try and attack it with your bare hands. Turn to **327**.

296

'Why do you ask about the coloured earths? Pretty, aren't they? It's an ornament, nothing more.'

The stinging of the bees is driving you mad. You are forced to make a dash for the ladder and run off, looking for a pool so you can immerse yourself and get rid of the bees. Turn to **197**.

297

The men have both spent much time in the forest and must know many of its secrets. They talk of the elves who do not deign to notice mortal men. Men say they are immortal yet they all look like children. The guide, Renard, mentions tree spirits and strange monsters. The hunter, Marek, tells you about a dragon, but Renard clearly doesn't believe the tale.

Both agree, however, that things are changing in the forest. The Westermen have come in their multitudes, hewing and burning the trees to feed iron monsters that belch smoke. Both men hate the Westermen.

'They are passing cruel – it's better to die in the forest than to be taken alive by the paleskins,' says Marek.

You become tired at last and ponder whether to stay at the inn (turn to **333**) or go home with Renard (turn to **224**).

298

You circle round to his vulnerable side and this gives you the opening you need. You can cut down in a slashing blow with your arm extended – a dangerous move that will still catch him if he springs back (turn to **377**). Or you can stab quickly at his midriff and dance back out of range again (turn to **364**).

299

'Yes it is I, the Lady in Grey. As you see I am also Elanor, the Lady of the Forest. I thought you had the wit to find your way this far. I am glad. The forest needs a hero. Climb up, take some elderflower nectar with me – you'll find it most refreshing. Did you need to play the flute?'

You climb up into the little tree-house. There is no furniture except a straw-filled hemp mattress to sleep on. The lady gestures you to sit in the nook of a curved branch, covered in dry moss, that serves as

a chair and is surprisingly comfortable. She sits on a small hammock made of creepers, and swings gently to and fro.

There are shelves made of thick ropes of creepers which have been trained to grow in and out around the edge of the tree-house. Behind the Lady in Grey on one of the shelves is a row of potions. The strange liquids with bright swirling colours look just as you imagine magical potions do. She looks deep into your eyes and says, 'Are you ready to be the forest's saviour?'

You can try to get the potions (turn to **341**). If you say you don't know what she is talking about and that you only came to get directions to the Tree of Knowledge, turn to **329**. Or you can say you would like to be the hero who saves the forest (turn to **9**).

300

You notice the Elf King making a swift pass with his hands as Huldranas takes the shot. This time it is as though the arrow veers in mid air to find its target. There is a distant crack of splintered wood and Huldranas' arrow stands quivering from the bough where your own arrow was embedded an instant earlier.

Immediately Huldranas whirls and flashes a sharp look at the king. He seems on the verge of saying something, but he is soon stared down by the millennial gaze of his liege lord. The Elf King turns to you and says shortly, 'You were a fool to choose this contest. What mortal could equal the archery of the elves?'

But as Huldranas passes you, he whispers in your ear, 'I cannot speak out against my king, mortal, but you and I shall always know the real result of this contest. You are my equal in this art.'

Turn to **69**.

301

You stomp through the undergrowth calling and searching but the only answer is the high mocking laughter of the elves as they recede into the depths of the forest. You have failed to meet the elves on Midsummer's Day.

You can try again tomorrow (turn to **139**), or

abandon all hope of persuading the elves to help save their own forest (turn to **280**).

302

Your confident declaration is greeted only by a look of wistful superiority. The Elf King suddenly strides forward and throws up his cloak, obscuring your vision in a rustle of soft green fabric. You smell something like honeysuckle and heather. Reaching up to pull aside the folds of the cloak, your fingers close only on a handful of fresh green leaves.

You look around. The elves have vanished. You have no choice but to turn and trudge through the trees, calling out for them to return. But your pleas are unanswered except by the song of birds and the murmuring of a distant brook. Turn to **78**.

303

If you have wounded Zorolotl three times, turn to **293**. If you have lost 7 or more Life Points, turn to **351**. Otherwise, turn to **415**.

304

'What is the white jelly? Is it a balm?'

Elanor hesitates. You wave the point of your sword in front of her nose but she won't talk.

You can try to kill her (turn to **253**), grab the bottle of white jelly and smear some on yourself (**242**), drink the red potion (**141**), or climb quickly down the ladder to the ground and run for it (turn to **197**).

305

You tell the chief it was very pleasant to meet up with an old friend again and wish him well, then take your leave.

As you walk towards the porch a man dressed in a black cloak walks brusquely past the guards, who obviously recognize him. The visitor is announced. 'It is Valerian the Moon Druid, sire, he says he has important news. Shall we let him come in?'

'Aye, let him.' The speech of the Westermen is guttural and uncouth-sounding but you can understand their dialect.

It is the man you first saw in the inn at Burg. He is still dressed in the black travelling cloak but his hood is thrown back to reveal the hatchet-like face and the pointed black goatee. He bows before the chief, then wrinkles his nose and stares at you.

Will you continue on your way (turn to **38**) or stay and hear what important news Valerian brings (turn to **4**)?

306

In stepping back from the cloud of vapours you have managed to hide yourself from the King of the Elves, who is even now casting another spell, but you have also stepped outside the ring and so lost the duel. The wind rips away the sheet of fog and the King of the Elves says: 'I am the victor, you have lost the duel.' He looks at you with contempt. 'Such magics as you can muster will not prevail over the Westermen. Leave the forest. You have a week to clear the edge of the forest or your life will be forfeit.'

With that the elves start to disappear into the trees. You turn your back on the clearing and start the long journey back to Burg. Turn to **384**.

307

Searching for the camp of the Westermen in the great forest takes several days. On the morning of the sixth day, breaking from the cover of orange-berried rowan trees, you see a steep-sided valley, charred and dead. The vegetation has been burned or dissolved away. In places bare rock has been exposed by heavy scuffing and here and there are smooth basins etched into the rock by strong chemicals. At the centre of the valley is a smooth green hillock about twenty feet high. At the far end is a strange, bare hill of some grey-white rock, looking like a mound of bone. An egret pecks at the green turf of the hillock for worms. The grass is lightly wreathed in mist.

Will you walk down into the dead valley past the blackened tree stumps (turn to **439**)? Or skirt around the valley to the east (turn to **429**)?

308

The elf draws a long slim dirk from his shirt and stabs you in the neck. You try to throw him off but it was a fatal wound: your blood gushes in crimson spurts to the ground. The forest is doomed.

309

You look hard into the Elf King's eyes despite the disquiet that his ageless gaze causes you. 'Well, sire, I've heard it said that he who speaks an elf's name can gain power over him . . .'

You do not see him move, yet none the less he seems to draw back away from you slightly. 'This is typical mortal talk,' he says guardedly, 'all bluff and bluster.'

Will you say the Elf King's name is: Arawn, (turn to **302**)? Eldring (turn to **387**)? Oberon (turn to **69**)? or Elivager (turn to **114**)?

310

'I am Elanor, the Lady of the Forest. Climb up here and take some elderflower nectar with me. The nectar of elderflowers is the most refreshing drink known to elf or man. My friends the bees collect it for me. You will find it most invigorating.

'I was watching you at the old inn in Burg. Do you remember the old woman in grey sitting in the shadows? I was searching for the forest's saviour. Is this the end of my quest? Are you the hero who will save the forest?'

You climb up into the little tree-house. There is no furniture inside but a straw-filled hempen sack to sleep on. The lady gestures you to sit in the nook of a curved branch, covered in dry moss, that serves as a chair: it is surprisingly comfortable. She sits on a small hammock made of creepers, and swings gently to and fro.

There are shelves made of thick ropes of creepers which have been trained to grow in and out around the edge of the tree-house. Behind the Lady in Grey on one of the shelves is a row of potions. The strange liquids with bright swirling colours look just as you imagine magical potions do.

You can try to get the potions (turn to **341**). Or you can say you don't know what she is talking about and that you only came for directions to the Tree of Knowledge (turn to **329**). If you want to say you would like to be the hero who saves the forest, turn to **9**.

311

You have made the wrong decision. Stunned as you are you are no match for this darting elf whose feet become a blur as he kicks you to the ground. You struggle to find your feet as he picks up the dirk and stabs into your neck with it. The pitiless elf has killed you.

312

You have gambled with your life and lost. Zorolotl's sword arcs through the air and buries itself in your skull. You fall to the ground, poleaxed. You are beyond the help of magic and the forest is doomed.

313

'What is the red potion? Does it banish pain?'

'Yes, how did you guess?' she replies.

Will you kill her (turn to **253**), grab the bottle of white jelly and smear some on yourself (turn to **242**), drink the red potion (turn to **141**), or climb quickly down the ladder to the ground and run off (turn to **197**)?

314

As you set foot on the hillock you are surprised at how hard the ground feels, yet it yields slightly, as if a layer of hard rock was resting on mud. The ground is smooth and has a sheen. It only looked like grass. You climb on up the hillock and reaching the summit, look down on its far side which is ribbed and ridged in the most unusual way. It dawns on you that the thing you are standing on is a gargantuan dragon. You can see its head, the size of a cart, curled up next to its feet as it slumbers. It seems not to have noticed you crawling like a fly over its great body.

Will you climb down to its head and slay it (turn to **74**)? Or will you attempt to wake it up and perhaps talk with it, for they say some dragons can talk (turn to **178**)?

315

The guard has chosen a place, where he is not observed by any of his fellows, to brutalize the slaves, so there will be no one to save him when you attack. Immersed as he is in his sadistic pleasures it is easy enough to walk up behind him and kill him before he even knows you are there, just as he was about to kick the innkeeper hard in the chest.

Taking the key from its chain about the dead guard's neck you free the slaves, including the innkeeper, and tell them to hide out in the forest. You tell the innkeeper of your visit to the inn at Burg and find out it is indeed his hostelry. He asks anxiously after his daughter and you are able to say she is tolerably well. 'She will be all the happier when you return to her, no doubt.'

'Will you come back with me to Burg? I will shower you with hospitality, a banquet fit for a prince . . .'

Will you escort the innkeeper safely back to his inn (turn to **62**) or tell him you must stay in the forest and foil the Westermen (turn to **378**)?

316

If you have SPELLS and wish to use one, turn to **355**. If you have UNARMED COMBAT turn to **368**. If you have SWORDPLAY, turn to **404**. If you have none of these skills, turn to **382**.

317

'What would you have us do? They outnumber us a hundred to one. Must we give battle? We have no swords.'

The elves know nothing of warfare. You will have to guide them. Many of them don't seem to believe the forest is really threatened.

Will you say that their bows alone are enough to guarantee victory, but first set out alone for the camp of the Westermen to find out what you can about your foes (turn to **307**)? Or will you suggest an expedition to capture swords from the forges (turn to **325**).

318

You break the spell with a word of negation and the cloud of gas evaporates. You were hardly affected by the choking poison gas. But your foe is casting another spell. Will you use a quick defensive charm (turn to **326**) or concentrate for longer on an attack spell (turn to **335**)?

319

Garoshtar swoops low, his wings cracking down at the last moment as he swings his head down and breathes over the leading company of soldiers, sending a cloud of poisonous gas and acid roiling about them. His wings crack hard against the air as he struggles to gain height, skimming the treetops. The mercenaries let loose their crossbows as one and Garoshtar is stuck like a pincushion. The dragon convulses in mid air, and it is all you can do to cling desperately on as he struggles to stay airborne. The wounds are not mortal but Garoshtar tells you he must land and sleep for a few years to heal his many hurts. He lands near Elvenhame and sinks immediately into a deep slumber, his bulk rising and falling in time with his breathing like a heavy ocean swell. You decide to search for the Elf King to report what has befallen brave Garoshtar. Turn to **57**.

320

Shot follows shot, with no clear sign which of you is the better archer. The elves look on in silence, giving no clue as to whether they are completely enraptured or whether they find the whole contest of no interest at all.

Your arm is beginning to tire; Huldranas shoots like an automaton, with precision and unflagging strength. You are wasting arrows, and you know that if you allow the contest to drag on you are going to lose through simple fatigue.

'Enough!' you say to the Elf King. 'It might amuse you elves to watch this carry on till the sky caves in, but the Westermen will not wait that long to bring about your Doomsday.'

'Very well,' he says. 'A more fraught duel, then – with life and death at stake.'

Turn to **18**.

321

You turn your back and start to run through the trees. Behind you the elf retrieves his dirk and sends it spinning end over end towards the small of your back. You hear it cutting through the air. If you have AGILITY you duck past a tree just in time, otherwise the dirk embeds itself in your back and you lose 3 Life Points. If you are still alive you can hear the elf shouting, 'Leave the forest. You are not wanted here.'

You can record the elven dirk among your possessions if you wish to keep it. Turn to **301**.

322

Elanor is nowhere to be seen, but her owl is still gazing at you unwinkingly. It follows as you exit the beautiful clearing, hoping to leave the bees behind. Just as you hear a loud buzzing behind you there is a stab of pain as a bee stings the back of your neck. Looking back you see a whole swarm of bees flying to attack you.

You can run in search of water to hide in (turn to **197**), smear some of the white jelly on yourself (turn to **184**), smear some of the black tar on yourself (turn to **168**), drink the blue potion (turn to **155**), or drink the red potion (turn to **141**).

323

'Then you'll be glad to stay a while to keep me company. I could help you, oh, I could, I could. But first you must make me like you.'

You protest that you are on an urgent and perilous quest.

'Spare me your excuses. You're just like all the rest. Nobody cares for the Kwerrel.' The impish little man hangs his head sadly. At length you ask how you can make him like you.

'By accepting my hospitality, by eating the flesh of the Blood of Iron toadstool.'

You hesitate. 'See, just like all the rest. You just can't find it in you to trust the Kwerrel, can you?'

You can eat the mushroom he offers you (turn to **138**) or refuse (turn to **438**).

324

The strange shadowy figure seems to know the forest. To your surprise he begins to tell you about the fabled Tree of Knowledge. 'Ah, yes, it is real enough. I myself have spoken with it and profited greatly thereby. The tree can give a man all the knowledge of the forest. It can teach magical charms as well. Do you seek this tree?' He doesn't wait for you to answer, but goes on, 'Then follow the Burgstream into the forest until it flows into the great Sirion river. Then turn east along the bank. Where the land rises climb until you reach a clearing and at its centre a cave. There you will find the guardian of the tree. Slay the guardian and the knowledge of the

tree will be yours. Farewell.'

With that he rises abruptly, twitches his black cloak around him and leaves the inn. The others all eye you suspiciously before leaving the common room.

You take a room at the inn for the night. Turn to **333**.

325

The expedition is a success but the strategy can only lead to failure. The gathering of all the elves at Elvenhame takes over a week. They are nearly ten thousand in all. The last to come are the solitary elves from the east, beyond the Widewater river. Some haven't been to Elvenhame for hundreds of years. Half are equipped with the captured swords, others with their powerful yew longbows.

They fight readily in pitched battle but are overwhelmed by the superior numbers and arms of the Westermen. The death of so many immortal elves is the greatest tragedy of all time. You are slain in the final battle: the forest is doomed.

326

As quick as thought you murmur the incantation of the magical Shield of Defence. You have just finished when the King of the Elves casts another spell. A luminous green halo pops forth from his fingertips and grows as it darts towards you. It splashes against the glowing defensive silver disk and fizzles out.

You can now cast Bafflement, Visceral Disruption or Tower of Will (turn to **347**), or maintain your Shield of Defence spell (turn to **123**).

327

As you get close to the Infernal Statue you realize there is nothing you can do against it with your bare hands. It must have been designed by a genius. There is no weak spot you can see. Your fists and feet pound the metal casing but it is only you who is getting hurt. You cannot even stop it chopping at the tree. It just ignores you as though you were no more than a flea. Several Westermen close in, intent on finishing you off while the machine destroys the tree. You will have to think of something else.

You can retreat to a safer spot and consider your strategy (turn to **144**), fight on where you are (turn to **409**), make a dash for the hose that connects the statue to the great boiler (turn to **397**), or spend a precious moment or two looking closely at the statue for a weakness (turn to **420**).

328

As soon as you mention the Tree of Knowledge the owl takes flight for the depths of the forest. If you have SPELLS and a wand you can try to stop it leaving you lost here (turn to 216) or you can shy a small stone at it (turn to 233). Otherwise you are alone again and must choose at random one of the many ways back into the forest (turn to 173).

329

She looks disappointed in you, almost crestfallen.

'Many a man has come in search of the tree. But only Valerian and I have gained its knowledge. What use is knowledge when the end of the world is at hand?' She seems to believe what she is saying.

If you decide she is mad and leave, turn to 98. If you want to listen to her, turn to 107.

330

You look away for a moment then sneak a look back towards the elf for a moment. You are too late. In a blink of the eye the last elf has vanished. You stomp through the undergrowth calling and searching but the only answer is the high mocking laughter of the elves as they recede into the depths of the forest. You have failed to meet the elves on Midsummer's Day.

You can try to meet the elves tomorrow (turn to 139) or abandon all hope of persuading the elves to help save their own forest (turn to 280).

331

The elf leads you as he said he would, never once attempting to escape and leave you lost in the depths of the forest. It is a journey of several hours through secret ways and tunnels. You notice him making signs now and again and realize he must be communicating with others of his kind, though you can see no one in the trees. Will you kill him before he can lead you into a trap (turn to **421**) or just follow in his footsteps (turn to **431**)?

332

'The mortal speaks the truth. If the forest is killed the whole world will die. It will not be the time of men but the time of death and desolation, the end of all things.'

'But what can we do? We number thousands but the Westermen come in hundreds of thousands.'

'Would you rather fight bravely, and show that you value the beauty that is your home? Or will you stand idly by and let the time of death and desolation come to the forest? I beg you to take up your bows and fight these cruel Westermen, not just for your own sake, but for all the world. We all need the forest in order to live.'

Turn to **317**.

333

The young girl, who says that her father is away on a journey to buy provisions, charges you a piece of gold for your food and for a night's lodging.

You sleep well and awake early but refreshed. Washing in cold water is invigorating and you enjoy the feel of the rough inn towel. There will be no such comforts in the forest.

Downstairs the inn is deserted. The woman in grey, the only other guest, has left already. The young girl is mopping the floor and she looks troubled. Asking what ails her brings the reply, 'My father did not return last night. I tried not to worry but I knew in my heart he wouldn't come. He went into the forest to buy provisions before the Westermen block the spice road. I know he has gone the way of the others. And that strange woman in grey never so much as touched her bed last night, though she didn't leave her room till after dawn. I begged Father to take Renard to guide him but he wouldn't spend the money. Now I'll never see him again.' With this, she breaks into tears.

As you comfort her, you ask the innkeeper's daughter to describe her father and say you will try to find either him or news of him. As you turn to leave she says, 'Fare you well, traveller, you are my only hope.' Turn to **210**.

334

Time has run out for the innkeeper. The next kick ruptures his spleen and the guard, swearing viciously, kicks him twice more then leaves him to bleed to death inwardly. There is nothing you can do for him. Thinking sadly of the poor innkeeper's daughter you turn your back on the camp of the Westermen and return to the forest. Soon the awful sights and sounds of the Westermen camp are far behind.

You can head west (turn to **43**), east (turn to **427**), south-west (turn to **70**), or south (turn to **78**) from here.

335

Before you can complete the train of thought you need for your spell, the King of the Elves has done so. A luminous green halo pops forth from his fingertips and grows as it darts towards you. It encircles your waist before you can move. Your legs feel as if they have turned to jelly and you cannot stop yourself collapsing to the ground.

'Submit, mortal, I have defeated you,' cries the King of the Elves.

Will you submit (turn to **255**) or try to fight on (turn to **272**)?

336

Three townsfolk leave as you curtly tell the man in black to mind his own business. The hunter and guide standing near the fire retreat into the kitchen. The woman in grey reaches for a gnarled old staff lying beneath her table and speaks for the first time. 'Mind your temper, Valerian. I will protect this stranger even if I must kill you.'

'You push your luck, old woman. What is the stranger to me? No one can hold up the progress of time. There is a new power astir in the forest. It will sweep you and all your beastly followers aside, like chaff in the wind.'

'There is no cause to fill the hearts of the good people of Burg with dismay. I know of what you speak.'

'Much good may the knowledge do you, old one. Haven't you heard the song of the wind? The time of man has come to the forest. All must pass away and change.' Valerian speaks the last words in such dire tones that the hunter, listening from behind the kitchen door, slams it shut in fear.

Valerian twitches his cloak around him and leaves abruptly, pausing only to look once more at you, as though committing your face to memory.

You can ask for a room in the inn for the night (turn to **333**) or sit at the table with the woman dressed in grey (turn to **181**).

The chief does not seem surprised you want to talk about what he calls the Tree of Life. He has been thinking about it himself a great deal. It seems he can't make up his mind whether to believe what Valerian the Moon Druid has told him. Valerian maintains the Tree of Life is the core of the elves' immortality. He counsels the chief to destroy the tree.

The chief is still talking animatedly when Valerian himself is ushered into the pavilion and announced by a guard. He is still wearing an all-enveloping black robe but its hood is thrown back to reveal his hatchet-like features and black goatee beard.

'It is Valerian the Moon Druid, sire. He says he has important news. Shall we let him come in?'

'Aye, let him.' The speech of the Westermen is guttural and uncouth-sounding but you can understand their dialect.

It is the man you first saw in the inn at Burg. He bows before the chief, then wrinkles his nose and stares in your general direction.

'I have driven off the tree bears, you will have no more trouble from them.' He sniffs again and moves his head from side to side while fixing his gaze just above your head, giving him a most comical air. The chief spreads out the map of the forest and his advisers gather round, almost blocking your exit.

Despite the risk, you wait to see if you can find out what they are planning. Turn to **4**.

338

As you speak the elf stoops, scoops up a handful of dirt and rotting leaves and hurls it into your face. You duck just in time and the handful of dirt spatters against a tree trunk behind you. Seizing your chance you shoulder-charge the elf, who is still trapped against the twin trees, and wrestle him to the ground. Feeling your strength, the elf surrenders to you and says he will take you to meet the elf lord. If you wish to keep his dagger, the elven dirk, note it on your Adventure sheet. Turn to **331**.

339

The Infernal Statue belches steam as its sword arm rises and falls like a piston. You review the spells you can cast against this terrible weapon of destruction.

Vanish (turn to **7**) allows you to disappear and move unseen. Choking Fog (turn to **31**) creates a cloud of poisonous gas. Visceral Disruption (turn to **64**) causes crippling stomach cramps. Shield of Defence (turn to **82**) is a defence against manifest magical attacks. Bafflement (turn to **113**) confuses your foe. Tower of Will (turn to **207**) subdues your enemy, who will then do your will.

The sword continues to drive into and out of the trunk of the Tree of Life. Green-stained wood flies up in splinters. Decide which spell you will cast and turn to the paragraph number indicated in brackets by its name.

340

'I cannot take you to Elvenhame. I would rather die like a mortal than reveal our last great secret.'

'What secret is that?' you ask.

'No mortal has ever looked upon the glory of Elvenhame.'

'And lived?' you ask grimly.

'No mortals live. If they did they wouldn't be mortal, would they?'

You threaten to kill the elf but he seems ready to die rather than to lead you to his lord. You look deep into his violet eyes, reading there the fear that you are about to cut short a life that should endure for millennia.

You can let him go (turn to **360**), tie him up (turn to **175**), or kill him anyway (turn to **370**).

341

You sidle towards the shelf while pretending to look about the little house with natural curiosity. Elanor watches you. As you get nearer she stands up and the hammock falls to the floor behind her. Her look challenges you to sit down. She will not let you near the potions.

You can attack her (turn to **389**) or sit down once more (turn to **9**).

342

At last you have picked a definite advantage by attacking Zorolotl's more vulnerable side. He defends as best he can but you are a brilliant swordsman and the point of your blade moves with hypnotizing speed. You slash him a vicious cut down the side of his body and he falls back. Turn to **303**.

343

You hurry quickly across the bridge as a last string of bubbles from Renard's body float to the surface. All is quiet behind you, but you do not look back, fearful of seeing the mangled remains of Renard bobbing in the stream. The path is difficult, overgrown and boggy. Every now and then you are hard put to decide which way it leads but by keeping fairly close to the great river you make progress for many hours until nightfall.

The noises of the forest seem to intensify with night, there is buzzing, clicking, croaking and the hoot of a lone owl to keep you company. Finding a dry place to rest is not easy but at last you find a mound of earth on which you can settle down.

If you have CHARMS and wish to turn your pendant into a warning stone, turn to **361**. Otherwise, turn to **419**.

344

You submit and Zorolotl holds his sword aloft in triumph. They give you a potion to drink which makes your body tingle excruciatingly but which cures you of all your wounds. Restore your Life Points to maximum. Turn to **163**.

345

'You mortals are used to battle. You hate, and wage wars constantly. Elf has never fought elf, we know nothing of war. We are thousands. The men of the west come in hundreds of thousands. What would you have us do?'

You can exhort them to fight (turn to **317**) or ask them what will happen if the Westermen raze the forest (turn to **332**).

346

As the Infernal Statue hacks through the trunk of the Tree of Life you cast Choking Fog: a cloud of noxious vapours surrounds the statue. The steam hissing from vents in the head dissipates the fog and the machine hacks on remorselessly, unaffected by your spell. One last great blow splits the trunk in the middle and the tree is dead. Losing all hope, you are taken prisoner and enslaved. The forest is doomed.

347

You concentrate on a potent attack spell. But which of the three images of the King of the Elves will you cast it at? None is moving so much as a flicker.

If you choose the right-hand one, turn to **149**. If you choose the centre one, turn to **132**. If you choose the left-hand one, turn to **121**.

348

It was a killing blow sure enough. Your sudden thrust takes Zorolotl by surprise and he is transfixed. Green blood runs down the shining metal of your sword blade and the violet eyes turn up into the top of the elf's head as he dies. There is a chilling low moan from the elves all around you. Turn to **263**.

349

The nearby elves look at you with horror. They had counted on you as their saviour in the moment of direst danger. The Infernal Statue strides slowly forward until it reaches the gigantic tree, dwarfed by it yet horribly menacing. The great sword rises and falls hewing great gashes out of the trunk. The elves moan as green sap begins to ooze rapidly from the scored Greenbark. There is a crash of thunder overhead and the horrible scene is plunged in gloom. You haven't long to act. The Infernal Statue will soon mortally wound the tree, and the Westermen are howling with fearful glee.

If you have SPELLS and a wand, you can turn to **339**. If you have SWORDPLAY and a sword, you can turn to **371**. If you have UNARMED COMBAT you can turn to **327**. If you wish to do something else, turn to **23**.

350

Beyond the black silk pavilion there are many smaller canvas tents roped to the few trees which have been allowed to stay standing. There is a regular bustle of people coming and going between the tents and the pavilion or riding in to report from scattered forges and slave encampments.

Will you try to get to the silk pavilion right away before you are spotted (turn to **239**) or stay hidden until dusk (turn to **217**)?

351

You have lost a lot of blood and the effort of fighting with such blood loss is making you dizzy. As Zoro-lotl moves carefully in to the attack again, your vision blurs.

Will you give up and submit, admitting you have lost the duel (turn to **344**)? Or fight on against the odds (turn to **312**)?

352

You cast the charm but the Lady in Grey just smiles at you. 'You cannot ensorcel me. I could ensorcel you, but that would not be to the purpose. Use your skills in the camp of the Westermen, not on me.' She is not impressed by your attempt to charm her. Turn to **9**.

353

The Elf King is retching helplessly on the forest floor. The look of horror on the faces of the other elves is of embarrassment and shame as much as fear for their king. You hurriedly speak the word of negation and the king begins to recover. You have won the duel (turn to **263**).

354

'There is trouble among the slaves from time to time. No more than usual. They are so far from home they fear for their lives even if they should escape. Of course we put to death those who try to escape, to discourage the others.'

'No trouble among the factions who serve under you here?'

'No, as long as there is no effective opposition, no war, no deaths, I don't have much to worry about. The other barons fear me and my infernal machine. Oh no, they don't want to take on The Steamer!'

You can ask about The Steamer (turn to **25**) or make your excuses and leave (turn to **305**).

355

Summoning forth all your will, you invoke one of the great words of power to stun the Embracer and so release Renard. Unfortunately, perhaps because the Embracer is underwater, nothing seems to happen. In fact you are at a loss to deal with the Embracer, which you can no longer see to aim a spell at. All you can do is carry on over the bridge, mourning the loss of poor Renard, your guide. You hadn't even paid him yet. Turn to **343**.

356

As you move in to wrestle him to the ground the elf stoops, scoops up a handful of dirt and rotting leaves and hurls it into your face. The dirt goes into your eyes and you recoil, rubbing at them. By the time you have rubbed the dirt away he has vanished. In the short time you couldn't see he couldn't have got far, so you search for him but his woodcraft is superior to yours and you cannot find him. Turn to **301**.

357

You draw the sword back and cut fast at Zorolotl's shoulder but he has time to regain his balance and skip lightly past your sword cut. The wavy edge of his blade runs against your thigh. Lose 4 Life Points as your red blood stains the ground; your foot feels hot and wet from the blood which soaks it. If you still live you jump back, *en garde* once more. Turn to **303**.

358

You say you remember the serving wench all right, but that you can't quite conjure up her name.

'She never was at the Reaver's. That's the girl from Rainbow's End.' The gleam in his eyes dims a moment to be replaced by a piercing look of low cunning. 'I don't think I remember you at all. Guards.'

You run for the exit to the porch but the guards cross their halberds in front of you, barring your way. Will you surrender (turn to **146**) or fight (turn to **17**)?

359

You must decide how you will face this monstrous machine of destruction. If you have SPELLS and a wand, you can turn to **339**. You can face it bare-handed or with UNARMED COMBAT: turn to **327**. If you have SWORDPLAY and a sword, you can turn to **295**. If you have CHARMS and an amulet you can turn to **391**. Or you can try something else: turn to **84**.

360

You tell the elf you are going to let him go and he seems grateful. 'I must speak with your lord; the forest and everything in it depends on it.'

'Then you must seek him, but beware: he will only speak to you today, Midsummer's Day. If you cannot find him before sundown we will kill you. Why meddle where mortals are not wanted? Leave the forest now, while you still have life. Now, look away please.'

You do so and when you look back seconds later he has vanished. Turn to **78**.

361

You perform the chant that makes the stone in your pendant grow warm if a large animal or beast should approach while you sleep. To your dismay the stone begins to heat up immediately you lie down to rest. You look around but can see nothing in the dark. You strain your ears but all you can hear are the usual night sounds of the forest. The stone grows hotter against your breast: the unseen danger is coming closer. The earth begins to vibrate beneath you as if a giant stalks you.

Will you try and hide by burying yourself in the earth mound (turn to **274**) or climb a nearby tree (turn to **392**)?

362

Speaking the word you clench your fist, imagining you are twisting and crushing the entrails of the Infernal Statue. The machine does not buckle or hold its stomach, as must a man affected by this puissant spell. Instead it lurches past the tree, then circles and lurches forward again, towards the deep blue pool. The cries of the Westermen die to silence and you can hear a muffled groaning from somewhere inside the Infernal Statue. It totters on the brink of the pool and then keels over into the water. There is a rush of steam like a geyser, followed by an explosion under-water as the machine tears itself apart. The Wester-men cry out in alarm and begin to retreat, harried by the arrows of the elves. Turn to **500**.

363

The elf is hampered by your gaze. It is as though your eyes have part-mesmerized him and you manage to back him up into a corner between two trees that have grown together. He tries a last attempt to get away but you cut him off and stand before him cutting off his escape.

You can press your advantage right away (turn to **356**) or give him the chance to surrender while remaining wary of any tricks (turn to **338**).

364

Your hurried stab pierces his clothing and thick green blood stains the tip of your blade. You have danced back out of range once again and you look to see if the wound will make Zorolotl submit. That smouldering look is still there in your eyes. The mandrake root he has eaten has indeed made him immune to pain.

Will you circle to the left of him (turn to **403**), to the right of him (turn to **393**), or meet him head on (turn to **257**)?

365

The King of the Elves is retching helplessly on the floor. The look of horror on the faces of the other elves is of embarrassment and shame as much as fear for their king. He can no longer even speak – this spell seems to have dire effects on elves. He is dying. The hard look on your face as he gives up the ghost with a ghoulish death rattle turns to one of fear as you realize the elves are going to kill you. You should have spared their king. Twenty arrows all find their mark in your body and you too are dead.

366

If you have the elven dirk and wish to throw it at the egret, turn to **288**. If you have SPELLS and wish to attack it with magic, turn to **278**. If you have CHARMS and an amulet, turn to **267**.

Otherwise there is nothing you can do to the wily bird, which keeps well out of range. You can, however, walk to the top of the hillock to see what you can see (turn to **314**) or leave the valley and skirt around it to the east (turn to **429**). If you have WILDERNESS LORE you can turn to **388**.

367

Your honesty stands you in good stead. The chief was trying to trick you for there never was any such a one-legged wench serving at the Reaver's Inn in Bessaraban. He is relaxed now; you can ask him whatever you like.

Will you ask him about the Tree of Knowledge (turn to **337**) or whether there is ever any trouble among the slaves or his own men (turn to **354**)?

368

You let yourself fall from the bridge into the murky waters and land, by chance, on top of Renard and the Embracer. The Embracer surges up out of the water once more to see what has assailed it, with you resting on its coiled tentacles. Renard is still struggling but his arms are pinioned by the Embracer's fibrous tentacles. You grab two flailing tentacles and haul yourself towards its cone-shaped head and smash your fist repeatedly between its murky grey eyes. Its coils loosen and Renard swims up to the surface. You follow, gasping for air as you break the surface, then swim to the far bank and scramble out before the man-eating monster can recover. Turn to **398**.

369

The statue is shaped like a man, bearing a ten-foot sword and clad head to toe in plate armour. Steam hisses out of vents behind its ears giving it a supernatural horror. The hose which joins it to the great boiler snakes out across the grass behind it, slithering on as the Infernal Statue takes slow strides towards the Tree of Life with the great sword held high.

You can rush between it and the Tree of Life (turn to **359**) or wait to see what it will do (turn to **349**).

370

The elf is powerless to run as you draw your dagger for the kill, but he can fight well enough. If you have SWORDPLAY and a sword, turn to **399**. If you have SPELLS and a wand, turn to **410**. If you have UNARMED COMBAT, turn to **405**. If you have none of these skills, turn to **308**.

371

The machine must have been designed by a genius: There is no weak spot you can see. Your sword rings and hammers against the statue's metal casing but you cannot even stop it chopping the tree. It just ignores you as though you were no more than a flea. Several Westermen close in towards you, intent on finishing you off while the machine destroys the tree. You will have to think of something else.

You can retreat to a safer spot while it is possible to do so and consider your strategy (turn to **144**), fight on where you are (turn to **84**), or make a dash for the hose connecting the statue to the great twenty-wheeled boiler (turn to **397**).

372

You speak the word and the spell wings its way to the Infernal Statue. It doesn't shake its head or rub its brow as a man affected by this spell might but it takes a great step backwards and falls into the deep blue pool.

There is a rush of steam like a geyser, followed by an explosion underwater as the machine tears itself apart. The Westermen cry out in alarm and begin to retreat, harried by the arrows of the elves. Turn to **500**.

373

Without warning you leap towards Elanor but she is ready for you. She tugs on the end of a vine and a secret hatch opens in the side of the tree-house. If you have AGILITY turn to **213**.

Otherwise, Elanor jumps through the hatch and swings to the ground on a hanging creeper.

'You will never leave the forest,' she warns you. 'I will turn every living thing in the forest against you.'

You are stung on the cheek by a bee. Then another stings your wrist. More bees fly in, buzzing angrily.

You can now take some of the potions, although you have time to grab only three. Choose which of the following you are taking: a clear cherry-red liquid in a stoppered phial, a small round bottle of something like runny tar, a jar of white jelly, a cloudy sea-blue fluid in a phial and a glass pot that contains bands of coloured earth. Note which three you are taking on your Adventure Sheet.

You rush to climb down the ladder to the ground. Turn to **322**.

374

The sword lops cleanly through the Embracer's tentacles but also bites deep into the softer flesh of Renard, your guide. The Embracer emits a piercing shriek and throws Renard at you before subsiding once more into the river. The water is stained livid red as Renard's heart pumps his lifeblood out. He flails desperately for help. Will you help him to the bank (turn to **246**) or abandon him (turn to **343**)?

375

Your sorcery does not work here inside the magical Umbellifer bush. Instead the bush itself seems to convulse and the imp falls to the ground out of sight. The thorny branches bow down from the central trunk and begin to sweep you along the ground towards the edge of the giant magical bush. It seems it doesn't like your magic and wants to spit you out. The thorns are pricking you but there is nothing you can do. You are completely engulfed. By the time you have been disgorged back into the forest you have lost 6 Life Points owing to loss of blood. If you still live, turn to **406**.

376

Somehow you kill one and leap over his falling body before it hits the ground. One stumbles over his slain brother in arms and balks those trying to follow. You escape to a nearby rock; from the safety of which you can scan the battle. The elves are at work with their arrows which zip and whine through the air, taking a terrible toll of the Westermen. The men's captains are driving them on out of the trees with whips.

The Infernal Statue lurches remorselessly towards the Tree of Life, its heavy step making the earth tremble. Its sword arm rises and falls like a piston as it hacks into the trunk of the great Greenbark tree. Thick green sap runs from the scores in the bark and there is another groan from the elves.

You can attack the machine before it kills the tree (turn to **359**) or try to reach the hose that connects it to the huge twenty-wheeled boiler behind it (turn to **397**).

377

Your slashing cut scores his shoulder but Zorolotl ripostes with a lancing blow into your side. You both spring away from each other, circling once more, as green and red blood flows freely. You have lost 5 Life Points. If you still live but wish to submit, turn to **422**; but if you are determined to fight on, turn to **303**.

378

You have moved to the edge of the trees now and look out over the grisly devastation. The innkeeper tells you his name is Pozzo and also reveals what he knows about the Westermen. Their leader has a huge scarlet and black pavilion tent beyond the forges where he plans how to despoil the forest. Pozzo offers to take you there.

Will you be guided by the innkeeper (turn to **428**) or return to the safety of the deep forest (turn to **282**)?

379

You return just in time to see a group of men surrounded by shieldbearers hewing down two great trees at the edge of the clearing. The air is alive with the whine and whoosh of the elven arrow shafts, many of which find their mark with uncanny accuracy, but whenever a Westerman drops to the ground two others take his place in the struggle to bring their engine of destruction to bear.

There is a groan of splitting wood matched by one from the elves as the beautiful trees crash to the ground and the Infernal Statue is revealed in all its terrifying metallic splendour. Turn to **390**.

380

Drawing breath you listen for others, realizing that at any moment you may be picked off by the arrows of his kind. You hurry quickly through the dense underbrush and stumble across a very strange old monument covered in creepers and partially knocked down by a fallen pine. It must once have been a great victory arch, perhaps built here before the forest itself grew here, or to commemorate a victory against rebels who had hidden out in the trees. Turn to **289**.

381

You fall back but his attack is pressed with such verve you have stepped outside the circle before you know where you are. Gathkeri stops and clasps his hands to his chest in triumph. 'I am the victor. You have stepped outside the circle and forfeited the duel.' Turn to **163**.

382

You let yourself fall from the bridge into the murky waters and land, by chance, on top of Renard and the Embracer. Renard is still struggling but his arms are pinioned by the man-eating monster's fibrous tentacles. Unfortunately it has more than enough tentacles to deal with you and soon your arms are crushed to your sides by what feel like iron bars. It drags you down to the slimy bottom and waits for you to drown, before feeding on your remains.

383

You charge to the attack but the elf dances aside even more quickly and his heel crashes into your side, breaking two of your ribs. Lose 2 Life Points. Each time you attack the elf turns your own strength against you until he sends you over his shoulder and you crash into the trunk of a fallen tree. Lose 3 more Life Points. If you are still alive, your head is muzzy from hitting the tree.

You can flee (turn to **321**) or fight on (turn to **311**).

384

You journey for several days falling more and more in love with the wild unpredictable beauty of the forest now that you know you may leave it. You turn back, risking all in one last attempt to persuade the elves to help save the forest. Turn to **78**.

385

There is a swift exchange of cut and thrust, which ends when the elf leaps back nimbly. You have wounded him again: there is more green blood on the tip of your sword, but there is red blood on the wavy-edged blade of Zorolotl. You have been wounded as well. Lose 4 Life Points. If you have lost 7 or more Life Points, turn to **351**. Otherwise the elf darts in to the attack again: turn to **415**.

386

You are led to the clearing in the centre of the city of trees and there sat down on the ground. The elves sit in tiers around you, perching on branches; more stand on the walkways and lean out from the towers between the trees. You cannot hide your awe at the natural beauty which surrounds you. When you say that you could never have imagined such an idyll they seem pleased.

'Never have we risked everything by sharing the beauty of our home with mortals. But now we realize that this beauty will soon be lost. In the time of men no one but you will tell tales of the splendours that were once Elvenhame.' There is a brooding melancholy in the faces of all the elves.

'But if you fight you can drive the men out of the forest.'

'Do you, a mortal, counsel us to slay your fellow men?'

What will you answer? That the men of the west are not your fellows (turn to **345**) or that the men are killing the forest which keeps the air pure for everyone to breathe (turn to **332**)?

387

He blinks slowly, as if clearing his head after a daze.

'Shall I speak it again?' you ask.

He holds up his hand. 'There is no need. You have named me truly, and in accordance with an ancient pact between myself and the first man I must now present you with my signet ring.' He takes off his ring and puts it into your hand. It is carved out of a single flawless emerald whose depths are filled with pinpoints of flaring green light. 'It is the symbol of my royal authority,' he says. 'To keep it would demonstrate a lack of goodwill on your part. Why not return it to me now, and then we shall talk.'

If you insist on retaining the ring, turn to **126**. If you return it to him, turn to **69**.

388

Until it stopped to watch you the white egret was definitely feeding. Egrets eat insects but there certainly wouldn't be many insects on the surface of a copper statue, no matter how green with age. You can only conclude that the colossus lying before you is not a statue but a sleeping dragon.

You can retreat hurriedly into the bog and let sleeping dragons lie (turn to 417) or you can go down into the valley and approach the monster (turn to 439).

389

If you have SPELLS and a wand, you can cast a Flamehand spell to drive her out of the tree-house (turn to 407). If you have SWORDPLAY you can threaten her by putting the tip of your sword to her throat (turn to 416). If you have CHARMS and an amulet you can try to enchant her so she sees you as a long lost friend (turn to 352). If you have none of these skills, you can tackle her to the floor and tie her up in the hammock (turn to 373).

390

The Westermen fall back behind their weapon of destruction and the shieldbearers cluster around the statue itself, behind which a great cylinder on huge wheels hisses and steams. The massive boiler is connected to the armoured statue by a hose. Suddenly a plume of steam rises out of the top of the statue's helmet with a shriek like a banshee, and its

face, which had been resting on its huge iron chest, slowly rises to look at the tree. There is a great roar from the Westermen. They look upon this thing with awe. It is their talisman, a moving demonstration of their invulnerability. Its powers to wreak havoc must be terrifying if a whole army of cruel slavers like the Westermen look upon it with such reverence.

Looking around you you see a look of bewilderment in the faces of the brave elves. No man can daunt them but nothing has prepared them to face this awful apparition from the underworld. Perhaps if you show the lead they will rally but for the moment at least you must face this Infernal Statue alone. Turn to **369**.

391

Your charms will not work on this metal monster. Your one hope is to attack it with your bare hands. Turn to **327**.

392

Just as you leave the mound of earth it collapses and the head of a Colossus beetle pokes out. Its head alone is twice as big as you and it shines blackly in the faint iridescence of nearby glow-worms. Its curving black horns are tipped with cruel crushing pincers. It lunges for you but you jump behind a tree and start to climb, hoping the beetle will not have the cunning to push the tree down and claim you as a tasty morsel.

It seems to lose track of you once you leave the

ground and at last retreats cumbersomely into its burrow, which it caps once more with masticated mud. (Turn to **237**).

393

You circle round to his sword side and are caught out by the speed of his darting lunge. The tip of his sword rips into your thigh and the elf has bounded out of range again before you can counter. Lose 4 Life Points. If you have lost 7 or more Life Points, turn to **351**. Otherwise, turn to **342** if you want to attack him on his vulnerable side, or turn to **385** if you want to meet him head to head.

394

It takes much longer to reach the tower than you imagined, since path after path leads you up against such obstacles as thorn bushes or fallen trees whose rotting bark crawls with insects. At last you pass into the open, where a clearing of uneven grassy ground stands between the louring ranks of trees.

The tower is outlined in a halo of moonlight which makes the angular masonry blocks gleam like silver. Ivy covers the walls in a dark tangled net. Under a lichen-stained armorial crest looms a great black door sealed with an iron lock. Gazing up, you see a glimmer of green light from the topmost chamber of the tower. It is the one sign that the place might not be abandoned and left to ruin.

If you have AGILITY and want to climb the tower, turn to **464**. If you have ROGUERY and want to pick the lock, turn to **489**. Otherwise, you can return to the main forest paths and continue on your way: turn to **454**.

395

You speak the word and bring forth the Choking Fog around the Infernal Machine. But why have you used this spell against a machine that doesn't breath but is powered by steam? The steam rushing from vents in the head dissipates the fog, and still the piston-like sword arm of the machine slices into the tree sending splinters of green wood into the air. You are wasting precious time. Now is your last chance to save the tree.

You can cast Bafflement (turn to **113**), Visceral Disruption (turn to **64**) or Tower of Will (turn to **186**).

396

As you struggle to your feet, cursing the very ground that has betrayed your feet, one of the guards breaks ranks and rushes towards you. As he closes, however, your opponent looks as if he is going to try to parry your blows rather than try to kill you himself, while his comrades close in on your back.

Will you risk all with a sudden lunge (turn to **453**) or fight him carefully, until you see an opening to attack without fear of a riposte (turn to **463**)?

397

A sudden leap not only carries you to where the hose lies unprotected on the ground but temporarily leaves your many assailants behind. You have one chance to sever the hose with your dagger. If you take it you will be surrounded by the enemy. Will you seize the moment to sever the hose (turn to **28**) or back off to nearby safer ground (turn to **144**)?

398

All is quiet behind you but you do not look back. Renard is anxious to leave the monster far behind and sets a cracking pace through the forest. The path is difficult, overgrown and boggy. You make slow progress for many hours until nightfall.

The noises of the forest seem to intensify with night: there is buzzing, clicking, croaking and the hoot of a lone owl to keep you company. Finding a dry place to rest is not easy but at last you find a mound of earth on which you can settle down.

'Not there!' exclaims Renard. 'That mound is the cap of the burrow of a Colossus beetle.'

Renard selects a place for you to camp for the night on a slope that climbs gradually away from the river. You take your calfskin boots off and wash your feet in a stream that winds between the trees. The boots are soaked wet and your feet show signs of a green mould which you wash off carefully. You are relieved when Renard says your journey on the morrow will take you up out of the river valley to drier parts.

'My journey?' you ask. 'What about you?'

'This is where I leave you. In the morning I will start back to Burg. You owe me six pieces of gold. Three days out, three days back. Tomorrow, walk past that old yew tree and go on, always seeking the higher ground. If you do that you will find what you seek at the hill top.'

'Why not guide me further?'

'I want to live a long time. Nothing would make me face the terrors of the Bonehill.' Renard is adamant he will go no further.

Will you pay Renard the price agreed (turn to **153**) or say that you will not pay him unless he takes you to the top of Bonehill (turn to **167**)?

399

The elf draws a long slim dirk from beneath his shirt. Your sword gives you the advantage of reach but you notice the elf is very agile and has remarkable balance. Will you press your attack fast with a mighty lunge (turn to **291**) or bide your time and keep him out of range with sword swipes while you gauge his style (turn to **271**)?

400

You direct the elves to shoot those who are clearing the path for the armed mass of soldiers behind and the Westermen are soon flinching and edging away. They are on the point of panic when there is a terrible groan from all of the elves. The Tree of Life has been slain and the elves have lost their immortality. As if they had been turned off by a master switch the elves all slump to the ground, stone dead. The forest is doomed.

401

Gathkeri begins to circle you warily once more; the murderous glint still gleams in his violet eyes.

Will you try to grapple him (turn to **142**) or attack him with your fists and feet (turn to **172**)?

402

The Greenbark trees here in Elvenhame are the biggest in the world. Their branches intermingle and there are walkways, galleries and towers perched on them. Elvenhame is a town in the trees. There are always flowers in bloom here, no matter what the season. Many coloured humming birds hover and dart from one soft spray of flowers to the next. The sound of their wings is like the soft music of a monk's chant. White hinds and black panthers lie together happily in the dappled sunlight beneath the trees.

Tree-houses spanning the gaps between the Greenbarks' great branches are decked with hanging violets and ivy. The bark of the trees shines like polished jade where it has been worn smooth by the passage of elven feet. There are hundreds of elves here, congregating quietly, astonished that a mortal has been brought to Elvenhame. Turn to **386**.

403

His wound has slowed him slightly. Even though you are trying the same trick again, you win the initiative. You have an opening for a killing blow. If you stab at his heart it will end things for the immortal elf (turn to **348**). If you flinch at killing him or do not want to, you can cut at his shoulder but this gives him more time to dodge (turn to **357**).

404

The smell of rot and marsh gas almost make you gag. The tips of the Embracer's tentacles wave in the air, almost as if they were trying to sniff you out.

You can slash at the tentacles coiled around Renard (turn to **374**), try to drive your sword point between its eyes (turn to **287**), or slash at the other tentacles it is preparing to coil around you (turn to **262**).

405

The elf draws a long slim dirk from beneath his shirt, but when he sees you coming at him without a weapon he throws the dirk back over his shoulder. This elf is quite tall but very lightly built: he does not look as strong as you. He moves very quickly and nimbly so you will have to be careful.

You can try to fell him with a sudden attack of kicks and lunges (turn to **383**) or try to back him up into a corner and then grapple with him (turn to **363**).

406

Sweat is pouring off you as you press through thick undergrowth, searching for the camp of the Wester-men. It is unnaturally hot here even though you occasionally glimpse the midday sun through gaps in the leaf canopy. The vegetation is lush and the ground spongy. Ants scuttle over everything. Here and there you see clumps of them swarming all over each other, eating hapless small creatures that have strayed.

As you push through thick ferns, brushing ants off as you go, there is a sudden whooshing noise ahead and to the left, followed by a strange loud gurgling. It sounded for all the world like a dragon. If you are near the Bonehill you must be several days' travel further east than you thought.

If you have WILDERNESS LORE, turn to **34**. If not, turn to **45**.

407

Spurting flame blossoms from your palm. Elanor tugs on a vine and a secret hatch opens in the side of the tree-house. She jumps through and swings to the ground on a hanging creeper.

'You will never leave the forest. I will turn every living thing in the forest against you.'

You are stung on the cheek by a bee. Then another stings your wrist. More bees fly in, buzzing angrily.

You can now take some of the potions, although

you have time to grab only three. Choose which of the following you are taking: a clear cherry-red liquid in a stoppered phial, a small round bottle of something like runny tar, a jar of white jelly, a cloudy sea-blue fluid in a phial and a glass pot that contains bands of coloured earth. Note which three you are taking on your Adventure Sheet.

You rush to climb down the ladder to the ground. Turn to **322**.

408

As you skirt the dead valley you can see the white egret standing atop the green hillock in the distance, watching you. As you slowly make progress you begin to see the other side of the hillock. It is creased and folded in a strange way. Then it hits you, it is so large you couldn't see it for what it was. Viewed from this side the hillock looks like a gargantuan copper statue, green with verdigris. There is a huge head tucked up next to massive claws. It is a statue of a dragon.

If you have WILDERNESS LORE, turn to **388**. If not, you can investigate it (turn to **439**) or enter the bogland and leave the monolithic statue behind (turn to **417**).

409

As soon as you wound one of them another takes his place. You fight like a hero but even heroes tire and at last one manages to sweep your legs out from under you. There is no escape as they finish you off with their swords.

410

Casting a spell while keeping your eyes fixed on the elf is not easy but you manage to utter the incantation of Entanglement and the underbrush beneath the elf grows suddenly. Low branches from the nearest tree seem to turn to rubber and stretch to wind themselves around the elf but he speaks his own word of power and then the fronds and branches wither and turn to ash, freeing him.

You begin another spell, a more powerful one this time, the spell of the Crushing Hand, but as you speak the elf stoops, scoops up a handful of dirt and rotting leaves and hurls it into your face. He has put you off the spell. The dirt goes into your eyes and you recoil, rubbing at them. By the time you have rubbed the dirt away he has vanished. In the short time you couldn't see he couldn't have got far, so you search for him but his woodcraft is superior to yours and you cannot find him. Turn to **380**.

The Greenbark trees here in Elvenhame are the biggest in the world. Their branches intermingle and there are walkways, galleries and towers perched on them. Elvenhame is a town in the trees. There are always flowers in bloom here, no matter what the season. Many coloured humming-birds hover and dart from one soft spray of flowers to the next. The sound of their wings is like the soft music of a monk's chant. White hinds and black panthers lie together happily in the dappled sunlight beneath the trees.

Bridges of tree-houses spanning the gaps between the Greenbarks' great branches are decked with hanging violets and ivy-lilies. The bark of the trees shines like polished jade where it has been worn smooth by the passage of elven feet. There are hundreds of elves here, congregating quietly, astonished that a mortal has been brought to Elvenhame.

Your guide takes you to the foot of a great ladder of oak poles, leading up to the king's pavilion which is decked out in silver and green. The poor elf who brought you to the hidden city is trembling as he stands nervously before his lord. If he is so frightened, you reason, you must be in great peril yourself. To your relief, the king asks him a series of questions in a tongue you cannot comprehend and seems quite satisfied with the answers. Turn to **386**.

412

You throw yourself at Gathkeri and your shoulder cannons into his hip. He sprawls flat on the ground and you jump astride his back. You are too strong for him to escape. The elf knows he is beaten.

'I submit,' he cries out loudly enough for all the elves to hear. 'You are the victor.'

You let him rise and you both walk over to the king. Turn to **263**.

413

The Westermen crossbowmen are outnumbered by the elves who are brilliant natural bowmen. While the crossbows take a minute to crank and reload, the best of the eleven marksmen can unleash ten arrows with just as much force as a crossbow. The first black rain of crossbow bolts claims a few elves but the rate of fire is too much for the Westermen who are too slow to take cover. It is a scene of butchery and the surviving mercenaries are soon put to flight.

The soldiers behind them regroup and start to raze the forest in front of them so they can advance on a wide front and bring their greater numbers to bear.

Will you organize the defence here (turn to **400**) or return to the other side of the great tree where you can hear a terrible racket and screaming (turn to **379**)?

414

When you awake you are still inside the great Umbellifer bush, lying beneath a twisted holly tree that is being uprooted by the growth of the bush. The Kwerrel imp has stolen everything off you but your clothes. If you had a sword you are now without it and there are no coins left in your money pouch, Anything else you may have picked up, except the emerald ring of the Lady of the Forest, if you have it, has been taken from you.

You start to dig again but again next morning you awake to find the hole filled in. You are hungry again and must eat. You lose track of time but nothing can daunt the spirit of a true hero and you persevere until the little Kwerrel tires of the great labour of undoing your day's work every night. By the time you have dug your way out the autumn rains have come. It begins to rain and rain and rain. You set off to the north once again. Turn to **406**.

415

Zorolotl strikes as fast as lightning. The point of his sword rips into your jerkin, but your riposte catches him on the neck. You have wounded the elf but you have also lost 3 Life Points. He advances warily again.

You can circle to the left of him (turn to **403**), to the right of him (turn to **393**), or meet him head on (turn to **385**).

416

With one neat fast movement you draw your sword and thrust the point an inch from Elanor's throat.

'What do you hope to gain by this?' she asks.

'The potions, what do they do?'

There are five potions on the shelf behind her. There is a clear cherry-red liquid in a wax-stoppered phial, a small round bottle of something like runny tar, a jar of white jelly, a cloudy sea-blue fluid in a phial and a glass pot containing layers of coloured earth.

Elanor starts to explain what each one does. 'The blue fluid, if quaffed in sunlight, will heal all save the most dire hurts.' As she says the word 'hurts', the back of your wrist, near the sword hilt, is stung by a bee. Elanor seems not to notice and goes on talking about the potions.

'This black tarry goo is the mulch of fire lizard's gizzard, a deadly poison.'

You are stung twice more, on the leg and the neck. More bees fly into the tree-house, buzzing angrily. You can't stand being stung like this for much longer. These bees are stinging with the ferocity of hornets.

Will you quickly ask about the red liquid (turn to **313**), the white jelly (turn to **304**), or the bands of coloured earth (turn to **296**) in the hope that one of them will protect against the insects? Or will you grab the phial of blue fluid and drink it (turn to **292**)?

417

The boglands are dangerous and it is slow going here. After a while you decide to struggle to higher ground and rejoin your old course. You make it to firmer ground at last, thinking to yourself you are lucky not to have been attacked by some of the gargantuan crocodiles you have seen swimming lazily in the deeper pools. Turn to **49**.

418

You have more sense than to smash the mirror here by the enchantress' bedside, where the noise would surely wake her. Taking it down carefully from the wall, you tiptoe to the balcony and drop it over the balustrade. You watch it flash in the moonlight as it falls to shatter on the ground far below. A gust of spring-scented wind arises and you catch a glimpse of an ethereal smiling face flitting up past you as a voice whispers, 'Thank you.' Then the wind dies and all is quiet again.

If you want to explore the bower further, turn to **470**. If you are ready to leave, turn to **479**.

419

You are rudely awakened when the earth mound that is your bed collapses beneath you. You try to puzzle out what has happened in the pitch dark. Then as the chitinous walls of a Colossus beetle's throat press you down towards its stomach you realize you have been swallowed alive while you slept. Nothing will avail you now as the acid of the beetle's stomach does its work. If only you had a guide who might have warned that the mound of earth on which you chose to sleep was the cap of a Colossus beetle's burrow.

420

Around the neck of the statue are four large screws which seem to be bolting the head to the body. You can leap up onto the statue and try to undo the screws and knock the helmet off (turn to **430**), fight on where you are (turn to **409**), or make a dash for the hose that connects the statue to the great boiler (turn to **192**).

421

You slay the unsuspecting elf easily enough but you are already trapped. Arrows zip and whine through the air and you are stuck like a pincushion. You die almost within sight of fabled Elvenhame.

422

You should have changed your tactics. Hampered by your smashed ribs you are an easier target for Gathkeri who bludgeons you to the ground with repeated blows to the head. You just have the sense left to submit before you lose consciousness. You have lost the duel. Turn to **163**.

423

You stand your ground bravely and the elves are ready to fight beside you, hidden in the trees, from where they can shoot with deadly accuracy. A group of men surrounded by shieldbearers shuffle forward and hew down two great trees at the edge of the clearing. The air is alive with the whine and whoosh of the elven arrow shafts, many of which find their mark with uncanny accuracy, but whenever a Westerman is dropped to the floor two others take his place in the struggle to bring their engine of destruction to bear.

There is a groan of splitting wood matched by one from the elves as the beautiful trees crash to the ground: the Infernal Statue is revealed in all its terrifying metallic splendour. Turn to **390**.

424

The toadstool is a dull red colour, spotted with purple. Underneath, the soft gills are mauve. The Kwerrel skips down to watch as you reach out to break off some toadstool flesh. You ask nervously whether it is poisonous.

'No, no, never, not poisonous, my dear, oh no.'

It tastes surprisingly good, it almost melts in your mouth. You begin to feel sleepy. You walk a few steps further then sit down with your back to the central trunk of the giant bush. Feeling warm, snug and content you fall into a deep sleep.

Turn to **414**.

425

You are stronger than Gathkeri. He wriggles and pushes against you but cannot break your grip. After a long struggle you manage to flip him onto his back on the ground and land astride him. You draw back your fist to strike but Gathkeri knows he is beaten. 'I submit,' he cries out loudly enough for all the elves to hear. 'You are the victor.' You let him rise and you both walk over to the Elf King. Turn to **263**.

426

You say that long life has worn out their spirit. 'Is that all there is to immortality, a long slide into the grey of uncaring? Look at the beauty all around you. Are your eyes worn out? Have you become blind to the glory of this forest? I've never seen anything like it.'

'Its glories are wasted on you, mortal.' The elf's voice cracks harshly and as he speaks your eyes fill with blood. Now it is you who is blind. You will never find your way out of the forest. Without sight you cannot even find food, and will surely perish in the forest.

427

After several days of trekking to the east you come to the banks of the grear Sirion river where it bends north before leaving the Forest of Arden. You have missed your way. You should have turned south if you wanted to reach the Bonehill, or south-west if you wanted to search for the bower of the lady of the woods. As it is you have wasted too much time, far out of your way. You plunge back into the green bosom of the forest. A few days later you start to find the fresh bodies of hundreds of elves among the trees. It is as though they have all been slain in a moment. The forest is doomed and so are you.

428

Pozzo takes you through the trees until you come to a large clearing. Noticing a steady stream of messengers riding post-haste to a point beyond the furnaces, you skirt round through the forest until, peering out between the branches of a Servis tree, you see a magnificent silk pavilion large enough to seat a hundred knights at a banquet. There are guards at each corner of the pavilion and two guards with halberds flank the silk porch which leads into the main tent. They are all dressed in rare steel armour and all have the sly look of the Westermen about them. It is a hundred paces across burned ground from the Servis tree to the tent.

If you have SPELLS and a wand, you can cast Vanish and sneak unseen into the pavilion (turn to **266**) or you can cast Friendship to charm your way past the guards and into their chief's confidence (turn to **231**). Otherwise, you can sneak up to the tent as a spy (turn to **350**).

429

You hug the rim of the valley heedless of the fact that you are breaking the skyline and thus easy to spot from afar. The forest is not dense here; large stagnant algae-covered pools, black watered and clogged with dead leaves, separate the trees.

If you are worried about being spotted and wish to descend into the bog land, turn to **417**. Or you can go back into the dead valley: turn to **408**.

430

You manage to scramble up the metal statue as it hacks on into the Tree of Life and start feverishly to take out the screw. Seeming to realize what you are trying to do, the machine brings its free arm down across your back to crush you. If you have AGILITY turn to **157**, otherwise turn to **290**.

431

At last you come across a well-trodden track, then climb a tree ladder. There is a maze of highways from tree to tree, fifty feet above the ground. Soon you are passing tree-houses festooned with flowering creepers and you see a hosts of elves staring at you. You are the first mortal to enter Elvenhame. Turn to **411**.

432

There is no trace of the archway by which you entered the great bush. It must have closed by magic. Your only way out is to dig or to break off branches until you have broken through to the forest outside.

You attack the branches but as soon as you break one off, two more grow magically in its place. The harder you work the further you are from freedom. You soon give up, there is no point in going on and so you will have to dig your way out. Alas, when you sleep, after digging hard for hours, the hole you have dug has been filled in once more. The footprints of the impish little Kwerrel show it was he who did it. There is no way out. In the end you have no choice but to eat part of the toadstool or faint through hunger. Turn to **424**.

433

You manage to spy on the leaders of the Westerman army but the chief has not come with them. He has sent a group of his warlords to do his dirty work for him while he leads a life of ease in his silken pavilion. Killing one or even several of the warlords will not stop the attack on the Tree of Life. You have squandered too much time. Nothing now can stop them slaying the Tree of Life. The forest is doomed.

434

A faint hissing can be heard above the heavy tramp of feet. The thick trees dampen sound so they must be very close. The Elf King and his subjects are ready in the branches with their bows. A few of the bravest elves gather around you beneath the great Greenbark trees. The Westermen have come to the Tree of Life. The fate of the whole world hangs in the balance. The hissing of their infernal engines grows louder, a foreign unnatural sound, a desecration of nature. Birds fly up from their path and the animals of the forest run in panic from the clanging metal monstrosities. The two columns of men are converging on the tree at the same time from opposite directions.

Will you stand your ground before the main column from which the hissing and clanging sounds come (turn to **423**)? Or will you make a stand first against the soldiers and crossbowmen in the smaller column (turn to **413**)?

435

You grab Gathkeri's throat but his arms are longer than yours and he punches you in the face, knocking you back off him. He has smashed your nose and red blood stains your jerkin as you totter momentarily on your knees, dazed and hurt. The elf is rising quickly to his feet.

You can throw yourself at him without getting up first (turn to **412**) or get up and move back out of immediate range (turn to **401**).

436

Something in what you have said has struck a chord with them.

'For thousands of years we have guarded our secret homes from the eyes of men. Now we must leave them and no one but us and the beasts of the woods will know or tell of the splendour that is Elvenhame. We grant you this, a sight of Elvenhame.'

You walk with them, they slow their pace for you, but they seem remarkably lacking in curiosity about you. It is as if they already know all they need to about the race of beings called man. It is a walk of several hours through secret ways and tunnels before the most beautiful sight in the world opens up before you. Turn to **402**.

437

The King of the Elves announces the start of the duel and Zorolotl advances carefully towards you. There is a smouldering, almost mesmerizing look in his dark violet eyes as if he had been chewing mandrake root to inure him to pain. He is left-handed like all the elves and he holds the blade point toward you like a rapier. There is certainly no fear of you in his eyes.

You can circle to the left of him (turn to **298**), to the right of him (turn to **393**), or meet him head on (turn to **415**).

During the fight, remember to keep a tally of the number of times you wound Zorolotl – if at all!

438

'Then I will hold you prisoner here for a day, or a month or a year . . . until I have grown tired of you.' With that the imp disappears high into the giant bush, his chirruping laughter mocking you. You start to look for a way out of the giant bush of thorns. Turn to **432**.

439

As you descend towards the bright green hillock the white egret starts to cackle and jumps up and down on the grass. As you approach it flies over the crest of the hillock but you can still hear it cackling on the other side. You look about warily in case the calls of the white bird have attracted any nearby men or elves. The valley is quiet.

If you would like to try to silence the egret, turn to **366**. If you simply walk to the top of the hillock to see what you can see, turn to **314**. If you leave the valley and skirt around it to the east, turn to **429**. If you have WILDERNESS LORE you can turn to **212**.

440

'It seems you will do little to save the forest by exploring its many paths,' says the owl. 'Where would you like to be taken?'

If you wish to follow the owl's directions to the camp of the Westermen, turn to **260**. If you have the two codewords *Bullhorn* and *Waterbearer* on your Adventure Sheet, you can follow the owl's directions to your allies (turn to **53**).

441

A silver noose flies up into the pavilion and darts through the air to hover above your head. Your magical shield blossoms beneath it and when they touch, both disappear with a musical pop. You run for the edge of the trees and are quickly lost in the forest once more, knowing they will never find you. The awful sights and sounds of the Westerman camp are soon far behind.

If you have the two codewords *Waterbearer* and *Bullhorn* on your Adventure Sheet, turn to **53**. Otherwise you can head west (turn to **43**), east (turn to **427**), south-west (turn to **70**), or south (turn to **78**) from here.

442

With the odds stacked against you, there is no time for subtle ploys. Quickly you cast Vanish, instantly disappearing from the gaze of your astonished foes. Lest they should hear you, however, you stealthily move from your current position, retreating to a safe vantage point at the edge of the forest so you can observe the confusion of the guards. Your Vanish spell wears off while you watch.

As the camp will be in a state of alert for some time, you reconsider your options.

If you wish to head west into the forest, turn to **43**. Or you can head east (turn to **427**), south-west (turn to **70**), or south (turn to **78**). If you wish to wait until nightfall and steal into the camp again under cover of darkness, turn to **217**.

443

The guard falls under your spell and you order him to protect you, but the Chief of the Westermen realizes something is amiss. He orders his guards to take you. Your guard is cut down by one of his own comrades. Unluckily for you these cruel Westermen care little for comradeship. Turn to **17**.

444

Shot follows shot, with no clear sign of which of you is the better archer. The elves look on in silence, giving no clue whether they are completely enraptured or whether they find the whole contest of no interest at all.

Your arm is beginning to tire; Huldranas shoots like an automaton, with precision and unflagging strength. You are wasting arrows, and you know that if you allow the contest to drag on you are going to lose through simple fatigue.

'Enough!' you say to the Elf King. 'It might amuse you elves to watch this carry on 'til the sky caves in, but the Westermen will not wait that long to bring about your Doomsday.'

'Very well,' he says. 'A more fraught duel, then – with life and death at stake.'

Turn to **18**.

445

You cast Choking Fog and a cloud of poisonous green gas explodes around you, filling the pavilion. You too suffer from the noxious effects of the gas. If you have 8 or more Life Points left, turn to **495**, otherwise turn to **472**.

446

Will you keep on the move as you fight, switching your attention to one of your assailants after the other (turn to **456**) or will you pound one into the ground before starting on the next (turn to **466**)?

447

The chief sounds as commanding as usual when he orders his men to give you safe escort to the edge of the forest. Valerian protests that you should be clapped in irons but the guards follow the chief's orders; you concentrate on subduing his mind until you are near the edge of the trees and almost out of range for the spell. You make a break for the trees as the chief at last throws off your domination and are lost to sight before he can recover his poise and issue new orders.

You are soon deep in the forest once more, knowing they will never find you. The awful sights and sounds of the Westerman camp are soon far behind. You can head west (turn to **43**), east (turn to **427**) south-west (turn to **70**), or south (turn to **78**) from here.

448

The Westermen don't trust the strange Moon Druid Valerian. They are all too ready to believe the mad sorcerer of the forest wishes their leader harm and has deprived their leader of their wits. They rush Valerian, but he utters the word 'Sanctuary' very loud and disappears with a single clap of his hands.

You shout instructions about how to care for their chief as you too make your escape.

You are quickly lost in the forest once more, safe in the knowledge that the guards will never find you. The awful sights and sounds of the Westerman camp are soon far behind. Will you head west (turn to **43**), east (turn to **427**), south-west (turn to **70**), or south (turn to **78**) from here?

449

You push the gossamer curtain aside and it rips as your fingers touch it, clinging to your skin. You suppress a gasp of disgust as you realize the fabric is not silk but spider's web. Nor is the bed anything like you expected. There are no silk cushions or satin sheets. Instead the bed's occupant lies on a layer of soil and leaf litter with huge purple night blooms growing all around her. She has the high elegant cheekbones and pointed ears that you imagine to be typical of elves. Her flesh is as white as lilies, and her glossy black hair is spread out across her pillow of loam like rootlets. The dim light makes her lips and long nails look as dark as old wine. You lean across her, listening to see if she is breathing or if she lies in the sleep of death . . .

'Over here,' a voice calls out softly, making you jump. You turn, scanning the deep shadows for signs of movement. There is no one there, but the voice calls again: 'Here.' It sounds like the tinkling of tiny bells.

You realize now where it is coming from: the mirror on the wall . . . Turn to **460**.

450

Which spell will you cast at this desperate time? You can cast Choking Fog (turn to **445**), Tower of Will (turn to **455**), Visions (turn to **465**), Bafflement (turn to **475**), or Visceral Disruption (turn to **468**).

451

Valerian completes a spell. A silver noose flies up into the pavilion and darts through the air to hover above your head. Before you can get any further, it drops over your head and tightens inexorably around your neck, throttling the life out of you.

452

You cast the Vanish spell and disappear. Then you creep slowly round to the porch of the pavilion and checking to make sure there will be no one coming in or out, you creep into the tent. The chief himself is sleeping on silken cushions of rich purple; his corpulent form is surrounded by the somnolent forms of his personal guards. Your keen senses also detect a faint shimmering in the air around these men

– a magical disturbance in the air that can only be some kind of warding. You had best be careful, for if you disturb it the guards could be on you in a trice.

Quietly you move to the table where the chief's maps are laid out in full view. The master map shows the Forest of Arden in its entirety. A broad swathe of brown has recently been painted across the green of the forest and a red point marks each of the Westermen encampments that are eating into the forest. Right in the centre of the triangle made by the Bonehill, the bower of the Lady of the Forest and the geysers, a small pool with an ancient-looking Greenbark tree drawn on it has been carefully painted in. Inked in by the tree is a simple note: 'Destroy the Tree of Life and the forest dies. The Steamer shall do the work.'

Dispatches lying ready for signing indicate the pincer movement that the Westermen will make on the tree – a cunning plan that could take any unwary defenders by surprise.

Write the codeword *Bullhorn* on your Adventure Sheet.

As your spell will fail in another ten minutes or so, you leave while the coast is clear. Turn to **95**.

453

Dire straits call for desperate measures and your gamble pays off. He falls to the ground, already dead before he strikes the sward. You whip your sword tip out of his body, jump over the fallen guard and run for the nearby trees. You are quickly lost in the forest once more, knowing the guards will never find you. The awful sights and sounds of the Westerman camp are soon far behind you.

Will you head west (turn to **43**), east (turn to **427**), south-west (turn to **70**), or south (turn to **78**) from here? Or will you wait until nightfall and steal into the camp again, (turn to **217**)?

Will you head west (turn to **43**), east (turn to **427**), south-west (turn to **70**), or south (turn to **78**)... (turn to **217**)?

454

As you walk on you find gaunt grey crags jutting up out of the forest. It is a relief to find clear landmarks at last. The forest is broken here; where the soil is thin above the grey rock only grass can grow, and you walk out of gloom into bright sunlight that hurts your eyes. There are countless paths leading back into the forest in all directions. As you stand contemplating the choice of ways a voice above and behind you says, 'Lost, are you?'

You turn round and look up. All you can see is a silver-feathered owl perched on top of an outcrop.

'Lost, are you?' the voice says again. It sounded as if the voice came from the owl but its beak didn't move.

Will you admit you are lost, (turn to **258**)? Or ignore it and walk on, choosing one of the many ways at random, (turn to **277**)?

Will you admit you are lost, (turn to **258**)? Or ignore it and walk on, choosing one of the many ways at random, (turn to **277**)?

455

You prepare to cast the Tower of Will spell, marshalling all your concentration. But who will you cast the spell at? At the Chief of the Westermen (turn to **482**), at Valerian (turn to **492**), or at the nearest guard who is twelve feet away (turn to **443**)?

456

The mercenary guards are heavy and slow, weighed down by their heavy chainmail corslets. Your lightning fast blows send one after another reeling but you will tire before you have defeated them all. Lose 3 Life Points, unless you have UNARMED COMBAT, in which case lose only 1 Life Point.

There is plenty of time for you to escape into the forest; however, none of them will dare to follow you into the shadows under the trees now that they have seen your prowess at the martial arts.

You are quickly lost in the forest once more, knowing they will never find you. The awful sights and sounds of the Westerman camp are soon far behind. Will you head west (turn to **43**), east (turn to **427**), south-west (turn to **70**), or south (turn to **78**) from here? Or will you wait until nightfall and steal into the camp again (turn to **217**)?

457

The chief sounds as commanding as usual when he orders his guard to kill Valerian, the Moon Druid. They hesitate for a moment and Valerian completes his spell. A silver noose flies up into the pavilion and darts through the air to hover above your head. One of the guards strikes Valerian down, but the noose drops over your head and tightens inexorably around your neck, throttling the life out of you.

458

In a moment you have cast the spell and a magical shield shimmers before you, like a ghostly buckler. A silver noose flies up into the pavilion and darts through the air to hover above your head. The shield floats up to intercept it and both disappear with a musical pop.

You must quickly choose another spell to cast. Will it be Tower of Will (turn to **455**), Visceral Disruption (turn to **478**), or Bafflement (turn to **475**)?

459

'Ah, if only you were a friend of the forest, I could help you,' says the owl. 'Have you still got the ring my lady gave you? Good, now put it on and perhaps I'll help you. Heroes need to have faith in their quest, you know.'

The owl's words have the ring of truth. Shamed, you put the ring onto your finger. Delete the codeword *Twinhead* and acquire the codeword *Crabclaw* instead.

'Well, I'm sure the forest is pleased to have you back on its side,' chides the owl. 'Why did it take you so long?'

Turn to **440**.

460

You gaze into the mirror. Your own image palely stares back from the limpid depths of the glass. Then it winks at you. 'I am a magic mirror,' it attests undeniably. 'Or, more precisely, I am an aerial sprite trapped within the polished crystal of the mirror. My mistress captured me long ago and keeps me to counsel her.'

You cast a wary glance over your shoulder, but the woman on the bed has not stirred. 'Who is she?' you whisper.

'An enchantress of the Fomorian race – more ancient than even the elves. She sleeps to preserve her unearthly beauty. Disturb her at your peril!'

You smile wryly. 'I have no intention of doing so.'

'Good.' In the mirror, your reflection returns your smile with a conspiratorial look. Leaning closer, it says: 'If you agree to break the mirror, thus releasing me from my long confinement, I'll grant one wish in return.'

If you refuse this suggestion, you can now either search the room (turn to **470**) or leave the tower (turn to **479**). If you accept, decide your wish. Will you ask for vitality (turn to **118**), wisdom (turn to **22**), or secret lore (turn to **268**)?

461

Eight guards have fanned out to encircle you. You can fall back quickly in the hope that they won't manage to close the circle in time (turn to **467**) or rush one of them, cut him down, and escape over his dead body (turn to **477**).

462

Using the cover provided by darkness, you creep slowly round to the porch of the pavilion and, waiting to make sure there is no one coming, you creep into the tent.

Inside, you see the chief himself is sleeping on silken cushions of rich purple; his corpulent form is surrounded by the somnolent forms of his personal guards. Your keen senses also detect a faint shimmering in the air around these men – a magical disturbance in the air that can only be some kind of warding. You had best be careful, for if you disturb it the guards could be on you in a trice.

Quietly you move to the table where the chief's maps are laid out in full view. The master map shows the Forest of Arden in its entirety. A broad swathe of brown has recently been painted across the green of the forest and a red point marks each of the Westermen encampments that are eating into the forest. Right in the centre of the triangle made by the Bonehill, the bower of the Lady of the Forest and the geysers, a small pool with an ancient-looking Green-bark tree drawn on it has been carefully painted in. Inked in by the tree is a simple note: 'Destroy the

Tree of Life and the forest dies. The Steamer shall do the work.'

Dispatches lying ready for signing indicate the pincer movement that the Westermen will make on the tree – a cunning plan that could take any unwary defenders by surprise.

Write the codeword *Bullhorn* on your Adventure Sheet.

You risk discovery the longer you remain here, so carefully considering what you have learned, you leave as soon as the coast is clear. Turn to **95**.

463

The man you are fighting is a bit of a coward and he guards carefully against your every move. You look like a pair of grannies circling each other warily. Time has run out for you. The guard's comrades close in from all sides and you are overwhelmed. You take two of them with you to the unending grey as the steel of their swords pierces your vitals and you fall, dying. The forest is doomed.

464

The stone blocks of the tower wall are fitted so closely that there is no toe-hold wider than a centipede's leg. The ivy helps you to begin your ascent, but it grows only sparsely on the upper part of the tower, where the stone remains as smooth as broken flint despite the centuries of wind and rain that must have scoured its surface. None but the most iron-nerved and nimble of adventurers could hope to make this ascent. Even you, for all your surefooted confidence, are careful not to glance down until you reach the parapet at the top of the tower and pull yourself over to safety.

An open arch leads from the balcony to the tower chamber. You step forward warily. Filtered through lattices of stonework, the moonbeams form a web of shadow across the smooth marble floor. Wan green light comes from a single flickering candle on a wrought-iron stand and behind it, on the far wall, a mirror sparkles with the fluid brilliance of quicksilver. A light breeze blows through the chamber carrying the odour of soil and growing things. As your eyes adjust further to the gloom, you can make out a figure sprawled across a bed surrounded by gossamer drapes.

If you tiptoe over to the bedside, turn to **449**. If you search the room, turn to **470**. If you go to take a closer look at the mirror, turn to **460**.

465

As you unleash your spell two perfect images of yourself appear in a puff of smoke to your left. Your attackers can't tell which one is the real you unless you move, for the visions remain motionless. Unfortunately the chief orders his men to bury their swords in all of the figures, including you. There is no escape and no time to cast another spell. The forest is doomed.

466

The nearest of these mercenary guards is no match for you. Your fists and feet are a blur of motion and you do indeed pummel him senseless, but the others close in and you are overwhelmed. You take two of them with you to the unending grey as the steel of their swords pierces your vitals and you fall, dying. The forest is doomed.

467

You fall back just in time and they form into two ranks before advancing towards you with military precision. Will you fall back again to the edge of the trees (**487**) or fight here (**497**)?

468

You are too late. Before you can complete your spell, Valerian has cast his. A silver noose flies up into the pavilion and darts through the air to hover above your head. One of the guards strikes Valerian down but the noose drops over your head and tightens inexorably around your neck, throttling the life out of you.

469

Your arrow strikes the very centre of the orchid. You turn a challenging look at Huldranas, but he does not notice. All his concentration is focused on the branch as he removes an arrow from his quiver and nocks on all in one graceful sinuous motion. As he draws back the bowstring, the muscles in his thin arms leap into sharp relief and you can see from his very posture that he is about to make a perfect shot.

If you push your skill to the very limits in an attempt to prove beyond argument who is the better archer, turn to **191**.

If you bide your time and take your shot when it is your turn, turn to **444**.

470

You discover a stout bronze chest in a vine-carpeted alcove. Your heart thuds with greed as you contemplate the lavish treasures it might contain. Alas, you are destined never to possess a single gold coin of that treasure. The moment you touch the hasp, the vine leaves start rustling of their own accord, making a noise like a hundred hissing serpents to break the silence of the bower. You should have guessed that the treasure chest would be protected by an alarm spell.

Turn to **499**.

471

You could try the famous charm Return of the Prodigal Son, to see if you can magically win their friendship (turn to **488**). Or you might try Fibonacci's Dweomer of Apprehension in the hope of scaring them so badly they will let you go (turn to **498**).

472

If you have CHARMS and an amulet, turn to **495**. Otherwise, you are too weak to withstand the effects of the gas and fall to the floor just as Valerian, the chief and the guards do. You are not the first to recover, owing to your weakened state, and the chief orders his men to take you. You cannot clear your head enough to cast another spell. Turn to **17**.

473

A bad choice. The men at either ends of the front rank move round and attack you from the back. You are quickly overwhelmed. You take two of them with you to the unending grey as the steel of their swords pierces your vitals and you fall, dying. The forest is doomed.

474

You fall back just in time and the guards form into two ranks before advancing towards you with military precision. Will you fall back again to the edge of the trees (turn to **494**) or fight here (turn to **446**)?

475

Will you cast Bafflement at the Chief of the Westermen (turn to **476**), Valerian the Moon Druid (turn to **486**), or at the nearest guard who is twelve feet away (turn to **496**)?

476

You hastily send the spell unseen across the space separating you from the Chief of the Westermen. As your spell takes hold the Chief of the Westermen stares about him uncomprehendingly. He is completely nonplussed. Valerian, however, is casting a spell. He stares at you intently and flourishes his arms menacingly. You haven't long to act.

Will you tell the guards Valerian has bewitched their chief (turn to **448**), or hastily cast Shield of Defence (turn to **458**) or Visceral Disruption (turn to **468**)?

477

The guards fall back before your sudden assault and close in again behind you. You are surrounded and overwhelmed. You take two of them with you to the unending grey but the steel of their swords pierces your vitals and you are quickly dispatched.

478

It is unfortunate for you that this powerful spell can be used against only one victim and you are surrounded by many aggressors. Even as one of them drops to the floor helpless, clutching his stomach, so the others close in and kill you.

479

You make your way quickly away from the eerie ivy-clad tower and return to the main track, where you snatch a few hours of rest before continuing on your way. Turn to **454**.

480

You have made the wrong choice. Why attack with your unguarded right side towards the enemy? You pay for your folly with a wicked thrust into your vitals that spills out your life force on the ground in front of the Westermen. The forest is doomed.

481

'What use is it to you, if you capture me? I have no gold, no treasures for you to steal – but I know where you can find some. The great dragon of the forest has breathed his last breath and I need the help of many men to carry away his hoard. We will be wealthy beyond the dreams of men – wealthier than kings. Will you help me? I'll give each of you a tenth of the bounty.'

They look at each other and one whispers something to his colleagues before saying he agrees. But you know enough of the ways of men to know it is just a trick – they clearly don't believe you and still mean to capture you.

If you have SWORDPLAY and wish to use it, turn to **461**. If you have CHARMS and wish to use one, turn to **471**. If you have SPELLS and wish to use one, turn to **442**. Otherwise, turn to **491**.

482

The indolent Chief of the Westermen falls under your spell. His mind is not as strong as yours and you can bend it to your will. Valerian is about to cast a spell. He stares at you intently and flourishes his arms menacingly.

You haven't long to act. Will you make the Chief of the Westermen order his guards to provide you safe escort into the forest (turn to **447**)? Or will you get him to order the guards to kill Valerian (turn to **457**)?

483

If you are left-handed, turn to **480**. If you are right-handed, turn to **490**.

484

The guards fall back before your sudden assault and close in again behind you. You are surrounded and overwhelmed. You take two of them with you to the unending grey but the steel of their sword pierces your vitals and you fall, dying. The forest is doomed.

485

You are halfway across the room when you hear an imperious voice raised in thunderous anger behind you. Glancing back, you see the lady of the tower rising from her bed. Soil and flower petals scatter to the marble floor as she raises her arms to the moonlight and sings the words of a spell. Suddenly a numbness creeps through your limbs and you see patches of grey mould spreading across the backs of your hands. With a horrified cry, you reel out of the chamber and stagger down the steps of the tower. Lose 4 Life Points because of the Noxious Blight spell (unless you have CHARMS and an amulet, in which case you can protect yourself and lose only 1 Life Point).

If you survive, the enchantress stands and watches you flee, sending peals of laughter ringing down the stairwell to mock you. The doors fly wide at your approach, but even on the threshold of escape you are frozen to the spot at the sound of her voice: 'Get you gone, mortal. If I catch you at my bedside a second time, your corpse will be food for my night-blooms.'

You stagger outside and the tower doors slam shut behind you. Turn to **479**.

486

You send the spell unseen across the space separating you from Valerian the Moon Druid. As your spell takes hold Valerian stares about him uncomprehendingly. He is completely nonplussed. Seizing your chance, you cast Vanish once more and make good your escape before Valerian can recover his wits.

You are quickly lost in the forest once more, knowing the guards will never find you. The awful sights and sounds of the Westerman camp are soon far behind. Will you head west (turn to **43**), east (turn to **427**), south-west (turn to **70**), or south (turn to **78**) from here?

487

You watch them warily as you fall back towards the forest's edge and don't notice a loose rock over which you trip. If you have AGILITY turn to **396**, otherwise by the time you have regained your feet they have surrounded you. You take two of them with you to the afterlife as the steel of their swords pierces your vitals and you fall, dying. The forest is doomed.

488

These common brutish men who have become so inured to the sufferings of their fellow men are almost devoid of any feelings of friendship. They look on you as a slave and nothing more. Their swords ring out of their sheaths and they are coming to get you.

If you have SPELLS and a wand, turn to **442**. If you have SWORDPLAY and a sword, turn to **461**. If you have UNARMED COMBAT you can turn to **491**. If you cannot defend yourself you have no choice but to surrender, turn to **151**.

489

Taking a long pin that you habitually keep in your boot, you delve into the lock with the deft precision of an expert jeweller. Despite its apparent age the mechanism of the lock is untouched by rust, and your efforts are soon rewarded with a heavy click as the lock springs open. You peer inside, but the moonlight only sketches a section of black marble floor, beyond which lies impenetrable darkness.

Groping your way, you find a balustrade and ascend the stairs with painstaking care. It would not do to miss your footing and go careering down in the dark.

A faint glimmer of viridescence warns you that you are nearing the top of the tower. You step through an archway into a chamber which is open to the night air. Filtered through lattices of stonework beside the balcony, moonbeams form a web of shadow across the marble floor. The wan green light you noticed before comes from a single flickering candle on a wrought-iron stand. On the far wall behind it, a mirror sparkles with a fluid brilliance like quicksilver. A light breeze blows through the chamber carrying the odour of soil and growing things. As your eyes adjust further to the gloom, you can make out a figure sprawled across a bed surrounded by gossamer drapes.

If you tiptoe over to the bedside (turn to **449**). If you search the room (turn to **470**). If you go to take a closer look at the mirror (turn to **460**).

490

You have made a good choice. You are attacking so that your weak side, the hand in which you are not holding your sword, is away from the enemy. By the time they close up to encircle you, your sword has already dropped three of them to the ground. Seeing your great prowess as a warrior they back off to look for reinforcements. You have plenty of time in which to make good your escape and are quickly lost in the forest once more, knowing they will never find you.

You can head west (turn to **43**), east (turn to **427**), south-west (turn to **70**), or south (turn to **78**) from here. Or you can wait until nightfall and steal into the camp again (turn to **217**).

491

Eight guards have fanned out to encircle you. If you fall back fast they might not manage to close the circle in time (turn to **474**). Or you could rush one of them, knock him down, and escape (turn to **484**).

492

The mind of Valerian the Moon Druid has been toughened by years in the wilderness. You are unable to subdue his mind before the Chief of the Westermen realizes something is amiss and orders his guards to take you. Turn to **17**.

493

If you are left-handed turn to **490**. If you are right-handed turn to **480**.

494

You watch them warily as you fall back towards the forest's edge and don't notice a loose rock over which you trip. If you have AGILITY turn to **396**, otherwise by the time you have regained your feet they have surrounded you. You take two of them with you to the afterlife but the steel of their swords pierces your vitals and you fall, dying. The forest is doomed.

495

You managed to gulp a large breath of air before you let off the spell, and were ready for the awful effects of the gas. You reach the portal of the pavilion and slip past the guards who are still retching hard. You are quickly lost in the forest once more, knowing they will never find you.

You can head west (turn to **43**), east (turn to **427**), south-west (turn to **70**), or south (turn to **78**) from here.

496

You send the spell unseen across the twelve feet of air separating you from the guard. As your spell takes hold the guard stares about him uncomprehendingly. He is completely nonplussed. Valerian, however, knows how to kill you. He stares at you intently and flourishes his arms menacingly. You haven't long to act. Will you cast Shield of Defence (turn to **458**) or Visceral Disruption (turn to **468**)?

497

They are in two ranks facing you. Will you attack the middle of the front rank (turn to **473**), the left end of the front rank of men (turn to **483**), or the right end of the front rank (turn to **493**)?

498

As you conjure the arcane dweomer, looks of perplexity cross the guards' faces. The looks are followed by anxiety, which finally turns to dread.

'It's an elf.'

'Is it an elf?'

'I feel strange.'

'It's using some unnatural magic.'

'Run.'

The man who says 'run' is the last one to move as they all turn tail and flee towards the tents of their comrades. They don't know what an elf looks like and obviously think you are one. They must be very frightened of the immortal spirits of the forest.

You have plenty of time in which to make good your escape. You are soon lost in the forest once more. Will you head west (turn to 43), east (turn to 427), south-west (turn to 70), or south (turn to 78) from here? Or you can wait until nightfall and steal into the camp again (turn to 217).

499

Stirring at the noise, the woman on the bed raises a slim white arm and brushes sleepily at her face. At any moment she will awaken. If she discovers you here, she might well express her surprise in a manner involving both magic and malice. You must begone with all stealth and haste.

If you have ROGUERY then you can use your skill to slip away unnoticed: turn to 479. Otherwise turn to 485.

500

The Westermen are routed. They have faced a dragon, the elves and a hero among mankind and they have had enough. They are easy to pick off as they flee through the forest much more slowly than the elves can follow. In their panic, they break into smaller and smaller groups and the elves have no difficulty in killing them. They show no mercy: the Westermen die in their tens of thousands. They will leave the forest, never to return. The Tree of Life lives on and Elanor and the elves will tend it till it has made a full recovery.

Without you, the elves and the whole forest would have been doomed. Without the forest the whole world's atmosphere would have been thrown into imbalance. Elanor greets you as the forest's saviour she had always known you would be. Now everything that grows in the great Forest of Arden is your friend. You will not be famous when you return to the lands of men. No one will ever know what great deeds you performed here, but it doesn't matter. You know you are a hero.

A Selected List of Fiction from Mammoth

While every effort is made to keep prices low, it is sometimes necessary to increase prices at short notice. Mandarin Paperbacks reserves the right to show new retail prices on covers which may differ from those previously advertised in the text or elsewhere.

The prices shown below were correct at the time of going to press.

☐	7497 0978 2	**Trial of Anna Cotman**	Vivien Alcock	£2.50
☐	7497 0712 7	**Under the Enchanter**	Nina Beachcroft	£2.50
☐	7497 0106 4	**Rescuing Gloria**	Gillian Cross	£2.50
☐	7497 0035 1	**The Animals of Farthing Wood**	Colin Dann	£3.50
☐	7497 0613 9	**The Cuckoo Plant**	Adam Ford	£3.50
☐	7497 0443 8	**Fast From the Gate**	Michael Hardcastle	£1.99
☐	7497 0136 6	**I Am David**	Anne Holm	£2.99
☐	7497 0295 8	**First Term**	Mary Hooper	£2.99
☐	7497 0033 5	**Lives of Christopher Chant**	Diana Wynne Jones	£2.99
☐	7497 0601 5	**The Revenge of Samuel Stokes**	Penelope Lively	£2.99
☐	7497 0344 X	**The Haunting**	Margaret Mahy	£2.99
☐	7497 0537 X	**Why The Whales Came**	Michael Morpurgo	£2.99
☐	7497 0831 X	**The Snow Spider**	Jenny Nimmo	£2.99
☐	7497 0992 8	**My Friend Flicka**	Mary O'Hara	£2.99
☐	7497 0525 6	**The Message**	Judith O'Neill	£2.99
☐	7497 0410 1	**Space Demons**	Gillian Rubinstein	£2.50
☐	7497 0151 X	**The Flawed Glass**	Ian Strachan	£2.99

All these books are available at your bookshop or newsagent, or can be ordered direct from the publisher. Just tick the titles you want and fill in the form below.

Mandarin Paperbacks, Cash Sales Department, PO Box 11, Falmouth, Cornwall TR10 9EN.

Please send cheque or postal order, no currency, for purchase price quoted and allow the following for postage and packing:

UK including BFPO	£1.00 for the first book, 50p for the second and 30p for each additional book ordered to a maximum charge of £3.00.
Overseas including Eire	£2 for the first book, £1.00 for the second and 50p for each additional book thereafter.

NAME (Block letters) ....

ADDRESS ....

....

☐ I enclose my remittance for ....

☐ I wish to pay by Access/Visa Card Number ☐☐☐☐☐☐☐☐☐☐☐☐☐☐☐☐

Expiry Date ☐☐☐☐